Into the Heart
of
Truth

by

John McAfee

Woodland
Publications

Credits

Editor: Jinny Ruths, Touchstone Publications

Production Managers: Pamela Jones, Maria Deelman

Cover Design: Gary Haney

Design and Production: Graphics West, Inc., Colorado Springs, Colorado

Printer: Kendall Printing, Greeley, Colorado

Copyright 2001 by Woodland Publications

Associate Publisher: Rogue Amazon Publications

Woodland Publications

2000 Arapaho Street
Woodland Park, Colorado 80863
EMAIL: support@woodlandpublications.com
WEBSITE: http://www.woodlandpublications.com

ISBN 0-9711569-1-3

Dedication

This book is dedicated to the legacies of Charles Darwin,
who showed us the infinite beauty
in the flowering of life;
to Ramana Maharshi, who pointed to the silence
in which all things exist;
and to Jiddu Krishnamurti, who shed such
brilliant light on the source of
ignorance and suffering.

*You have your truth,
and another theirs.
They are equally false.
The only real truth
belongs to no one.*

Tai Tsung,
second emperor of
the Tang dynasty

Contents

Introduction   3

PART ONE
The Importance of Relationship

❁
───────────

Chapter One
The Meaning of Relationship   11

Chapter Two
The World and Ourselves   19

Chapter Three
The Me of Relationship   25

Chapter Four
The Substance of Self.   35

Chapter Five
Thought and Self   47

Chapter Six
We Are the World.   53

PART TWO
The Fabric of the Self

❖

Chapter Seven

Self-Perception 65

Chapter Eight

The Creation of Our Self-Image 71

Chapter Nine

The Forces of Change 79

Chapter Ten

The Relationship Between Images 85

Chapter Eleven

The Projection of Self-Image 91

Chapter Twelve

Change 99

PART THREE
Relational Yoga

❖

Chapter Thirteen

The Path of Yoga 111

Chapter Fourteen

The Body 119

Chapter Fifteen

The Breath 125

Chapter Sixteen

The Intellect 131

Chapter Seventeen

The Process of Breathing. 137

Chapter Eighteen

Meditation and Self-Understanding. 143

Chapter Nineteen

Ujjayi Meditation 149

Chapter Twenty

Breath and Relationship 159

Chapter Twenty-One

The Understanding. 165

Chapter Twenty-Two

The Practice of Relational Yoga 171

Chapter Twenty-Three

Further Inquiry 175

Appendix A: Ujjayi Breathing 185

List of Illustrations 189

About Truth

Is there an absolute truth, a fundamental reality that is capable of being perceived, or is all truth relative? If truth is relative, then it is individualistic—it is something that is filtered through our individual prejudices and limited by our sense inputs—and it is therefore fragmentary, tainted, and incomplete. So can it be the truth? Something that is incomplete or twisted by our prejudices is obviously less than the truth. Yet all our knowledge, by definition, is fragmentary and tainted by bias. The known by its very nature is relative and therefore limited.

Each of us lives in the field of the known, of all things past. If you watch the process of perception in yourself, you find that every experience, act, and sensation that comes to your awareness is first filtered through the background of your own conditioning. Experience is interpreted as it happens, and our interpretations are based on our unique system of beliefs, fears, cravings and anticipations, and our past experiences in similar situations.

We may think that only the paranoid or unbalanced have twisted perceptions, but we would be wrong. Each of us is a bundle of opinions, beliefs, and ideals that tell us what is "true" in people's intents; we overflow with fears and suspicions that tell us the "truth" of people's actions; we are full of pride and self-importance that tell us the "truth" of our own being.

We have all known the beauty of love, for example. But invariably, we soon begin to feel possessive of our love's object, and the possessiveness leads to jealousy, and then to anger; yet we continue to insist that we love. But can possessiveness, jealousy, and anger co-exist with love? Clearly not. They are mutually exclusive. The one destroys the other. Love eradicates all personal hatreds and jealousies, and where jealousy or possessiveness exists, love cannot. Yet we still insist to ourselves and to others that we love. But if we look deeply enough, we will find that the root of our supposed love is our individual need for security, contentment or pleasure, or that it keeps fear or discomfort at bay. We use the object of love as a distraction against the unpleasant or as a stimulus to pleasure. Cruel words perhaps, but please don't simply reject them out of hand. Look into yourself, without judgment or condemnation, but with simple observation. It is our condemnation that has created this inability to see the truth in ourselves.

Likewise, we are violent and antagonistic; yet the filter of our perceptions allows us to believe that we are not, either through justification of our principles and ideals or through blindness to our actions. We are envious and jealous; yet we perceive these qualities as ambition or a healthy competitive drive. We are filled with greed for material goods or even spiritual progress, and as we accumulate we tell ourselves that we are being successful. We divide ourselves from others through vanity or feelings of superiority, and still pretend to be teachers and leaders. We filter everything that we know of ourselves through the sieve of our self-constructed self-image. We create in our minds similar images of our spouses, children, neighbors, friends, and enemies. In truth, all of our relationships are between our self-made image and the images we construct of other people. These images relate as if they possessed a life and reality of their own. How are we to know truth in these relationships?

Given our situation with regard to truth, is there in fact anything more? Must we forever struggle blindly in the field of our own and others' deceptions, or is there not some absolute truth, some reality that exists independent of our past conditioning, which can be discovered? I say unconditionally that there is, and that it is hidden in the mirror of our existing relationship to the world.

Relational Yoga is based on the principle of bringing the practice of yoga into our everyday activities—into our relationships. In order to do this we must first understand the true nature of our relationship to the world. Then we must understand something about who is doing the relating—ourselves. Finally, we must know how to bring the practice of yoga into our everyday lives to help complete our relationship to the world in a way that creates intelligence, beauty, and compassion.

This book has been divided into three parts to address each of the issues above. It is important to read each part in the sequence presented in order to reap the most from this book.

*W*hich truth of the
matter would you have
sir? There are so many
of them.

Charles Cotterell

Introduction

Of all the questions we can ~~pose, the most~~ fascinating and rewarding is "Who am I?" Yet the question never occurs to most of us. If it does, then it seems meaningless or even ridiculous at first glance. We certainly know our name, our sex, our age. We know our image in the mirror and our physical characteristics. We know our profession and our marital status. We can rattle off whatever titles and honors we may possess and can name our talents and pastimes. With all of this knowledge, at any moment we can come up with a word, a phrase, or an idea that tells us who we are. We are doctors, engineers, or business people. We are fathers or mothers, brothers or sisters. We are intellectuals or we are simple people. We have a name, a form, and a list of qualities and characteristics that come easily to mind. If we practice medicine we *are* doctors. If we have children we *are* parents. If our name is called out, we *are* that person. So the question "Who am I?" seems at first absurd or at least insignificant.

The reason that the question "Who am I?" seems to lack significance is that we seek to answer it with words, or with images and ideas. We ask the question and we look for an answer that the intellect can validate. We want to reason the answer out—find some concept that stands up to logic—or provide some verbal description. It is as if we have never seen sunlight but answer "What is sunlight?" with a mental concept, based only on what we have heard or inferred about the nature of sunlight. But to know sunlight we must go outside and open our eyes. No amount of logic, no word, no image will ever show us sunlight, and we can never feel its warmth through the idea of temperature.

Yet what are all of these images and concepts that come to mind when we look at ourselves? What do we mean when we say we are business people, writers, actors, or politicians? What is the significance of our name, our physical form, or our self-descriptions? If you practice engineering, for example, does the word "engineer" really provide a definitive description of who you are? It describes something that you have *done* or something that you *know*. It implies that you have a store of knowledge relevant to engineering and have spent time applying that knowledge to specific situations. It says something about your memories and possibly your daily activities. But does it reveal who you *are*, your essential being? If you are in a room full of engineers, you may each call yourself an engineer, but you will nevertheless each feel a unique individuality separate from the others. Moreover, this sense of uniqueness will not diminish if all of you are also parents, joggers, part-time writers, the same sex, and holders of the same educational degree. No matter how many qualities or characteristics you share with someone, you never feel that you and that person are in fact the same person. Whatever words we use to describe ourselves, we do not confuse ourselves with others who use identical words to describe themselves.

We identify strongly with our name and respond instinctively to the question "Who are you?" with our given names—I am John, or Sue, or whatever. But certainly the name is just a word, and others share the same name. There are no inherent, internal qualities of identity to a name. No quality of "Sue-ness" or "John-ness" can be isolated.

Our physical form, as we see it in the mirror, is a mental image we carry around with us—a picture, a concept. And this concept changes as we change our appearance. But it should be apparent that this internal image, in many cases, matches the external reality imperfectly at best. How many of us continue to picture ourselves in our youthful form as we age well past any recognition of it? And how many of us dress or groom ourselves in an absurd manner while carrying an internal image of good taste? We frequently create a self-image free of physical faults that are obvious to others; or instead, we imagine faults that do not exist—we think we are obese when in fact we are thin, or consider ourselves unattractive while others find us beautiful. It is this internal image of our physical form with which we identify, rather than the physical form itself. Yet, if we choose to respond to the question "Who am I?" with the answer "I am the physical form of my body", then what do we really mean? This answer is either a sequence of words that amuse and satisfy the intellect, or the internal image of the physical form that we ourselves have created. But the internal image of our form cannot be considered to *be* who we are any more than the word "engineer" can be considered to be who we are.

The question "Who am I?" cannot be answered with words. The answer is not an idea. It is not a concept or a logical construct. It is not some verbal description lurking in our memory banks waiting to be retrieved, as we might retrieve the name of the capital of Idaho. Yet such a description is what we generally attempt when we address the question to ourselves. We attempt to fish from memory an appropriate sequence of words or ideas that gives us an answer. But if we assume that, whatever we may be, we are at least as real as a ray of sunlight or a tree, then we should be able to know *that* reality beyond the realm of mere ideas. We should be able to peel back the veil of words and directly see—to perceive with tangible insight—the truth of ourselves. If the "I" has no reality beyond words or images, then we are nothing but an idea. In that case we can know nothing tangible about ourselves other than the fact that we exist as an idea—and even this by itself would be a powerful revelation. But if the "I" does have a reality beyond words, then we should be able to answer "Who am I?" with that reality.

This book is directed to those interested in answering this most fundamental of questions. Do not think that it can answer the question for you. If this book could provide them, such answers would only be ideas, words, or images, and your mind is most likely full of these things already. The challenge for you is to seek the reality behind the words and descriptions. This book can be nothing more than a signpost in that quest.

The practice of Relational Yoga, if used properly, can be a powerful tool that can help unlock the mysteries of our selves. My hope is that you use the tool appropriately, and that you approach the quest in earnest. However, the tool, without the full understanding of our relationship to the world—and therefore how to apply the tool—is of little use. It is therefore extremely important to fully grasp the first two sections of this book before beginning the practice.

Part One

✱

The
Importance
of
Relationship

Truth has no special time of its own. Its hour is now—always.

Albert Schweizer

Chapter 1

The Meaning of Relationship

Maslow

All of life is relationship, and it is how we relate to people, to things, to ideas, and to our past actions that defines who we are. We measure ourselves in relation to others and act toward others according to our internal standards of their, and our own, personal worth. Our relationship to our possessions causes fear and anxiety, or a sense of security and well-being. Our relationship to our ideas—cultural, religious, social, moral—provides a basis for making decisions and judging our progress through life. And our relationship to our past and continuing actions is the source of our pride or shame.

All of our actions in life are in relationship to something. There can be no action in the absence of relationship. When we buy, sell, hoard, give away, covet, admire, reject, or use material goods we are relating to the material world—the world of things. Lust, anger, envy, jealousy, love, hate: all require an object of relationship—another human being. Even our daydreams and private thoughts can only exist in relationship to other thoughts, or to our desires, fears, or pleasures.

It is through relationship that we assert our personal identities, and it is in the mirror of relationship that we see ourselves and know our natures.

Most of us are oblivious to the real nature of our relationship to the world. We know that we meet people and they become our friends, enemies, casual acquaintances, or we are indifferent to them. We like some people and are attracted to them, and we dislike others and reject them. We are suspicious of some and trusting of others. We care deeply for a few and for the majority we have little feeling. Some relationships are casual and short-lived, while others are deeper and longer lasting. Each of us has a multitude of relationships with family, neighbors, friends, business associates, and casual contacts; we know that this swirl of relationships is constantly changing. We drop one friend and collect another. Our "best" friends become less than best. Our relationship with our girlfriend, boyfriend or spouse is no longer functioning satisfactorily, so we redefine the relationship or find a replacement. We are unhappy with our boss and look for a new job. Our relationship with our neighbors may cycle between tolerance and hostility.

We are aware of the constant flux of our relationships and the pain, antagonism, and confusion that this instability engenders. But how many of us are aware of the internal forces that define our relationships and cause such chaos and turmoil? It is important to understand the mechanisms of relationship because all of life is an unending movement in relationship. If we do not understand the reality of our relationships, then we are isolated. We perpetuate the national, cultural, and religious divisions within society, which in turn create individuals who are divided in themselves.

In seeking to understand relationship, you must begin with yourself. Have you ever asked what is the single, constant, and abiding interest in your life? It is yourself. Aren't each of us concerned first and foremost with our own self-centered activities, our personal vanities, our ambition, our achievements and success? Don't we perpetually pursue our own happiness or security, and perpetually defend our own idiosyncrasies? Our egotistical pursuits, our desire to attain, to possess, are our constant companions, and they breed our equally constant jealousies, envies, and antagonisms. Our personal drive and competition feed our insatiable greed. We are plagued by our own tortures and despairs; our life, if we are at all aware, is a constant running away from our own loneliness.

We each live in our own world; we are at every moment concerned with ourselves, and from this basis of self-involvement we attempt to relate to the world. We seek inner security through outward relationship: each one depending on another for comfort, companionship, or pleasure. We use relationship as a means of escape from loneliness. We use one another.

Can there be relationship if each of us is focused on our own personal pursuits, if we depend on others for our comfort or pleasure? Can we love if we lead separate lives in growing isolation, pursuing self-centered activities? Can we have any sort of relationship if we construct walls of resistance around ourselves?

We claim to love, but our love is based primarily on sex or pleasure, personal security or need. We find escape through love, or seek to fill some internal void. For most, love is a means to some end, a method to gain happiness or to sustain some ideal. And with it generally come the attendant jealousies and possessiveness. If our love relationships lack true depth, bring jealousy and anger, and offer only limited harmony, then what hope have we for any other relationship?

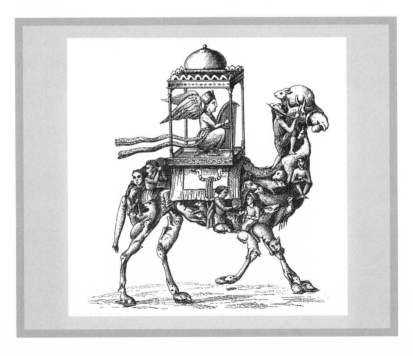

If we examine our relationships, we will discover that invariably they are grounded in our own self-interests. We choose friends because they amuse us, give us pleasure, flatter us, or fill some need for companionship. When this amusement or pleasure ceases, we find reasons to avoid them. Our husbands, wives, or partners provide sex, financial support, help with children, someone to rely on. They give us a sense of permanence in relationship; our feelings of love, supported by the pleasures afforded through marriage, give a strong, though frequently illusory, sense of purpose to life. Our relationship to those we work for is based on either ambition or fear. With our neighbors, relationships are based on a desire to avoid conflict. All of our relationships, from the most casual to the most lasting, are based on either pleasure or fear. This self-centered basis of relationship is the cause of our loneliness and isolation.

Our relationships bring exploitation, because they are instruments of gratification. But true relationship is based on communion, and there can be no communion where there is exploitation. Because of this, our relationships are fragmented, incomplete; they create unending conflict. They cause division within ourselves and propagate divisions between individuals. Our relationships divide instead of join.

Relationship is society. And we have created a society whose structure is based on mutual use, mutual gratification, and acquisitiveness. We have created a world of cruelty, hostility, and war through our relationships, and society is in crisis. But the crisis is not just in the outer world: it is in human consciousness itself. We each live in and are conscious only of our own isolated world, and true relationship, true cooperation eludes us.

It is imperative that each of us discovers his or her true relationship to the world. If we do not, we have no hope of ending the perpetual cycle of war, hostility, and hatred that threatens to end humankind's very existence.

Chapter 2

The World and Ourselves

What is this world that we live in, the world that consumes our attentions and to which we struggle to relate? How was it created? What sustains it?

We live in the world of humankind, the world of social structure. It is the world of business, politics, industry, and social and economic striving. It is the world divided into nations, cultures, races, religions, and ethnic groups. It is a world filled with ambitions and possessiveness, antagonisms and hatreds. It is a world of increasing knowledge and decreasing harmony. It is the world of education, science, art, and history. It is the world of relationships between competing ideals, dogmas, and beliefs; between competing cultures and religions; between individuals and states. It is the world of family and friends, jobs and responsibilities; and our concern in life is how to relate to this world in a way that brings us the greatest happiness or the least pain and fear.

We have created this world. It is a reflection of each of us. Each person's inner ambitions are reflected in society as national expansion. Our inner anger and violence are revealed as state or cultural hostility and war. Our inner conflicts find worldwide expression as conflicting laws, changing moralities, or social chaos. As we are petty, narrow, and bigoted, so are our institutions, religions, states, and national groups. How could it be otherwise? These nations, religions, and institutions are made up of individuals. We each create the collective through our need to belong, through identification, through our ambitions, fears, and desire for security. The collective does not exist apart from the individual. And as the individual is, so is the collective, only magnified by the number of individuals that comprise it. Individual hostility is measured in words or by blows of the fist. National hostility is measured in terms of genocide, mass suffering, and devastation. Individual greed is limited by each person's reach and grasp. National greed has no end to acquisitiveness through taxation, levies, border expansion, or nationalizations. It is the same with all of our institutions. Even religious institutions reflect our inner struggles. How many wars are rooted in religious conflict?

You might say that others have created this human-caused suffering in the world and that you have nothing to do with it. You might say that you are different, that you are even working to change things for the better, that you don't possess the same fears, hatreds, and ambitions as others. You may think yourself superior, wiser, more loving and compassionate. You may feel that a few ill-informed or morally corrupt persons of power cause conflict and struggle in the world, and that things could be made better if these people were removed or replaced. But who gave these people their power? The masses seek leaders just like themselves.

Or you may feel that world conflict is caused by misinformation or by people misguided by untrue beliefs, misled by unworkable ideals. You insist that harmony can be created by the correct knowledge, religion, or belief system. But what knowledge will lead to this harmony? What system of beliefs can unite the world? We are still full of hate, anger, and greed in spite of our beliefs; we still fear; we are still ambitious and possessive.

We have, each of us, created this world. There are no exceptions. And the world in turn has created us. We are the result of all of the world's past conflicts, its past corruptions. The society created by our parents and grandparents is the society in which we live. Its structure of individual and group ambition, greed and acquisitiveness, has not changed in substance. All that changes is the outward form—rituals, fashions, and social habits. The world has created us and we are each identical in our fundamental natures. Our driving forces—fear, pleasure, desire, and ambition—are common to all mankind. We may express them through individual idiosyncrasies, and they may be colored by our culture, religion, or ethnicity, but we cannot claim uniqueness.

We have created a world of conflict through our own self-centered activities, and that world of conflict, in turn, has created self-centeredness in the individual as a natural response to conflict. It is an unending circle. Our relationship to the world will continue to be one of conflict and illusion as long as we relate from our center of selfishness. We must find a new point of reference.

Chapter 3

The Me of Relationship

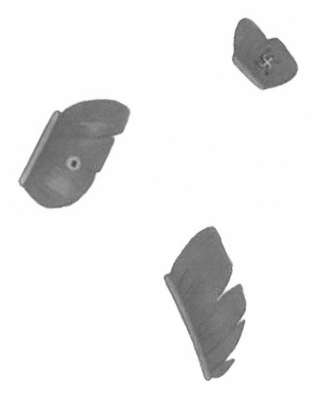

Who or what are we? It's an obvious question once we set about the task of understanding our relationship to the world. What is it that seeks to relate to the world: the form of our body, our personality, our collection of fears and desires, our past experiences, our actions, our subconscious, or our soul, whatever that may be? What is it exactly that has a relationship with the world that is causing such conflict and strife, such suffering and misery? You may shrug off the question as absurd, saying, "Obviously, it is myself." But what do you mean by that? It's not a rhetorical inquiry. It is a serious question, for if we don't understand the substance and form of the thing, that self that relates through conflict, then we have no hope of real change.

If we investigate our sense of "I" and "mine," what do we find first? We notice its separateness: there is "me," and then there is everything else. The entire world, its billions of people, its commerce, industry and noise, its structures and organizations—all these constitute "everything else." On one side is "me," and the entire known universe is on the other. It is a laughably unbalanced equation. It becomes even more absurd when we consider the enormous importance we give to the "me"; for the rest of the known universe we are concerned only with those few elements that enlarge or amuse the "me."

So we have drawn an invisible line that defines us. Everything on this side of the line is identified as "me," and everything on the other side is identified as "not me," and the line becomes a boundary behind which we lead our tiny existences. Once we have recognized that it is there, it seems natural to try to locate the line. But this is a difficult process. The line is hazy and fragmentary; it is in constant motion. In searching for the line that separates you from the world, you may find the division is unclear. The line does not exist in a form that can be isolated; the "I" is of a form and substance that are illusory.

Let's look at a simple example. When you identify your feelings with a group or a cause, you begin to behave as if the group were an extension of yourself. When the group is violated, you feel violated; when the group is threatened, you feel threatened. When you are with the group, your identity becomes hazy; you feel the collective thrills and exuberance, the collective anger. In the moment of group action, if you are aware, your self is identified entirely with the group. Group hatreds become your hatreds, group laughter your laughter. You might rationalize this by saying that you were merely cooperating with the group, or were temporarily caught up in group excitement, but that you still existed as a separate "I" identified with your individual body. But if you observe yourself carefully, you will see that this is not the case. This is not to say that the individual body and personality do not exist in the group, because obviously they do. But the "I" sense is not limited to that.

We have drawn a line to separate the "me" from the world, and for convenience we each tacitly understand the line to be the boundary of our bodies. Everything inside the body is us, and everything outside is not us. We have a sense

of "internal" and "external." Wherever we find the body, we also find ourselves. It is a convenient and practical demarcation. Yet if we look closely, we find that it is false. If our bodies are injured, for example, we feel the pain, but we consider the pain as something separate from the "I." The pain is something that happens *to* us; it is not part of us. We feel separate from the pain, even though we suffer from it. Our perceptions of all bodily sensations are the same. We find them pleasant or unpleasant—something that happens to us, something we enjoy or avoid—but they are not the "me." It is as if the "I" is observing, controlling, and feeling our bodies; it is some separate entity that is affected by the body but still separate from it. The body doesn't seem to be "me" at all. If we lose the function of a bodily part—or even the part itself—temporarily or otherwise, our sense of "me" doesn't change. The "I" still wants, desires, needs, feels, hopes, and fears, with unabated potency. It still separates itself from the world. In fact, on close inspection, we can find nothing that the "I" does not separate itself from. It seems to have circumscribed a line so tight that everything in existence lives happily on the "not me" side, with nothing whatsoever on the "me" side. A great deal *belongs* to the "me": my hopes, my desires, my wealth, my spouse, my property, my job, my feelings, ad infinitum. But the thing to which all this belongs, the "I," is certainly a mystery.

Yet still we have a sense of "me," a sense of "I" as separate and central. And we have certainly drawn a distinction between that sense and the "not me." All of our actions, thoughts, desires, and fears indicate that the "I" exists separate from the rest of life. But if we cannot identify this line of separation, or perhaps comprehend that it does not exist in its assumed form, then we will never know the boundaries of this entity that relates to the world and will never be able to change the conflict that exists through that relationship.

The greatest difficulty in establishing the line of demarcation between the "I" and everything else is caused by the process of identification. The "I," the ego, divides the world into itself and all else, and then proceeds to co-opt as much of the "all else" as it can. It identifies with certain external elements of life—religious groups, cultural organizations, nations, and states—and those elements become part of the "me," or at least part of the "mine." We see this especially in our relationships to our children and loved ones. We risk our lives to save our children if necessary, and things that happen to them affect us as much as if the event had happened to us. We feel hurt when they are in pain. We are happy with their happiness. Our thoughts and actions include them, just as we think of ourselves or act in our own self-interest. So the ego, under some circumstances, expands outward, taking in families, possessions, social and political organizations, and as much of the "not me" as it safely can. But this process of identification with another is tenuous and subject to sudden change and shrinkage. Any threat to identification, such as being abandoned by a wife or husband, brings first a defense reaction—an attempt to save the identification—or if this fails, then a sudden withdrawal. The identification ceases and the ego retreats. This entire process of identification is made more mysterious by the fact that those whom we co-opt as part of our sense of "I" have, in turn, their own sense of "I," and they have likely co-opted us as part of themselves. These constant forays by the ego, to seek out and claim fragments of life as part of itself, make the task of identifying the substance of this self highly problematic.

If we watch this process of identification and retreat, we see that the co-opting is only a surface phenomenon with the ego. It does not stand up to close scrutiny. Like our bodily sensations, our identifications with other fragments of life are not truly parts of the "me" but are only things happening *to* the "me." The "me" continues to evade our view. We have not truly included another person in our sense of self through identification; we have only expanded the ego through the idea of inclusion. We have expanded ourselves through the activity of thoughts—through thinking. But the substance of the self, if there is any, has not changed.

This phenomenon occurs even when we *feel* that the self, the "I," is identified with something larger. Our thoughts create the idea of group consciousness, and we feel we are the group. In reality this limited self, this divider, is again merely trying to enlarge itself. It has created a division in which all of life is seen as "not me," and from the isolation and poverty of this position it perpetually attempts to expand itself. But its insistence on separateness, on the division that creates it as a separate, distinct entity, is the very cause of its isolation, its emptiness, its loneliness. It wants to exist as a

unique creation, with its own will and destiny, and that desire is the root of all suffering and conflict. It is a limited, finite entity, yet it seeks to absorb all of infinite life into itself. If it would end the separation, however, then the self would find itself in the heart of infinity.

Chapter 4

The Substance of Self

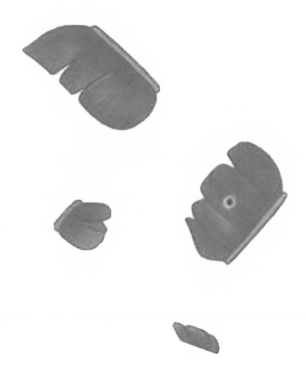

When I speak of self, from this point on, I am not speaking of some transcendental Self, a higher Self that we reach through enlightenment or grace or a Self that we identify with God, or truth, or ultimate reality. I neither deny nor assert the truth of such a Self. If it exists, then no words are capable of describing it. No images are adequate or useful. No explanations could relate anything of value concerning this Self. Such a Self by definition is infinite, timeless, and unconditioned; but knowledge, words, and images are finite, conditioned, and bounded by time, so such a Self cannot be known, in our normal sense of knowing. It cannot be contained as knowledge or words in a finite brain. No mental image or spiritual idea will convey the truth of this Self. Any experience of such a Self is beyond knowledge and can never be transmitted or explained to another. Any attempt to address this infinite Self will merely cause the ego to create internal images and approximations of it and to desire the attainment of such an imagined Self for itself, thereby making the ego larger and more self-important, and therefore more separate and isolated. It is the age-old problem: we want to know God, but have little interest in knowing our selves, because our selves are small, poverty-ridden, pitiful entities that do not stand up to the light of scrutiny. If a timeless, infinite, unconditioned state of living exists, it is this pitiful self that prevents the experience of it through its divisive and separative activities. But if we instead choose to know and understand this limited, finite, petty self that isolates itself from the world, invents the "I," and creates our conflicts, we can come to a state of understanding in which the unknown, whatever that may be, can reveal itself.

Because most of us have heard the psychological descriptions and definitions of the word "ego," we already have images and ideas in our minds about its meaning, so let's forget at this point that we know it. From this point on we want to discover, for ourselves, the true nature of the entity that is creating separation and conflict between the world and ourselves. We don't have to name it. We are aware of our sense

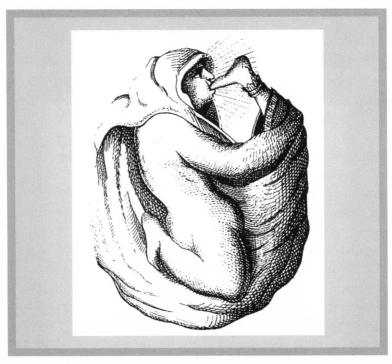

of separation and selfishness, and we live the conflict it produces, so there is a reality that we can investigate independent of words, prior concepts, and definitions. Nothing is needed except our willingness to look.

We have ascertained that our selves are divisive. We separate ourselves from the world and treat ourselves differently than we treat everything that is not ourselves. We agonize over our personal fears or thwarted ambitions, while we watch the deaths and sufferings of countless millions with near indifference. We may say, "what a pity" or even shed a tear, but we quickly return to our own petty miseries—our lost jobs or dwindling bank accounts. So the self has divided the world and placed disproportionate importance on that tiny piece it has carved out for the "I." But what other things can we find out about this self?

The self is extremely concerned with the idea of continuity. The self existed yesterday, exists now, and hopes to exist tomorrow. It sees itself as a continuous thread of consciousness with no beginning and, hopefully, no end. The intellect, of course, sometimes entertains the thought that the "me" may not have existed prior to birth and may not continue after death, but the cunning self has answers for this. It is important for the self to have continuity, to stretch into the past and the future, for without this continuity it has no basis for existence. The self is made up, at least partially, of all of our past experiences—hurts, pleasures, fears, losses, and gains. Our basic personalities are a composite of the past. We are conditioned by the past. We have created formulas for living and meet each event in life armed with our past experiences, with our knowledge based in the past and with preconceived courses of action. The self is intricately woven into this fabric of past experiences, and it requires the continued existence of this past, through our memories, in order to continue its own existence.

The future is also a necessary component of the self. Desiring continuity, the self structures its actions in the present to maintain its existence in the future. It judges every choice in life on the basis of its continuance. Thus it approves of greed, possessiveness, and hoarding on the basis that these increase its chance of survival if external events turn sour. It feels sorry for the suffering and death in much of the world,

but secretly is thankful that it is not part of it. It plans, and cunningly works toward a future in which it still exists. In its quest for continuity, it is quick to adopt religious or philo-sophical systems that promise immortality.

The self is also expansive, perpetually seeking to enlarge itself. It is always attempting to become more, greater, better. This divisive, continuous self is forever becoming something. Regardless of its possessions or securities, it always seeks something more. At the core of this self is emptiness, and it believes that the emptiness can be filled if only the right circumstances or situation are achieved. It thinks that if we were more knowledgeable, or wealthier, or more spiritual, we would have peace. If our talents were greater, or our looks more attractive, we could find happiness. In this constant quest for greater knowledge, wisdom or pleasure lies the hope of attaining some vaguely defined state of perfection or grace. The self is restless, in constant motion, forever seeking. It is unsatisfied except for brief moments here and there that quickly become part of the web of the past.

When we look closely we find that the self is divisive, continuous, and expansive. These qualities make up the core of the self. We have already seen that the quality of separation is hazy and ill defined—the line dividing the self from the world cannot be clearly defined or described. Will we fare better with the quality of continuity? The self wants to continue, but what does this mean exactly? What is continuity in relation to the self?

The self is interwoven with the past, as we have seen. But the past exists only in memories. Our experiences in each present moment are recorded in memory, and this memory is the basis for our thinking. We would not be able to think without memory. The existence of this sentence would be

impossible without the words stored in my brain and remembered. We would not be able to find our way home, recognize our families, or know how to use a spoon without memory. But does the past as recorded in our memories actually exist? Obviously not. We might remember a summer flower garden in the midst of winter, and raise images of its fragrance and visual beauty, but the snow of winter is the only current reality. The fragrance and visual beauty no longer exist. They may return in a varied form next summer or they may not, but they do not exist in the present moment of winter. Yet the self acts otherwise, as if the thread of its consciousness is still active in the past. We each raise images of past experiences and re-live them, with modifications, in the present moment. We remember an event and actually feel the event as if it were happening in the present. When we remember a past insult we feel anger and resentment in the present moment. When we remember a past sexual conquest we are aroused in the present. And when we remember a past loss we bring a feeling of sorrow into the present. The past is, for the self, a storehouse of experiences to be relived, to be continued. And as though reliving an experience were not enough, the self projects those past experiences into the future and makes plans to have them again. Past experiences are continued through reliving or planning for the future. But this reliving of the past is merely a process of thinking. Does it have any basis in reality outside of our thoughts? Does this continuity of the self through past experiences have any substance or tangible form? Is it real? Certainly, thinking is real, but is the self then nothing more than a thought process, a modification of memory?

When the self plans the future based on past experiences, it frequently attempts to modify these experiences to make them better, more complete, more pleasurable, or more permanent. It removes unpleasant aspects and adds more pleasurable aspects. This process is an expression of the self's quality of expansion. Experience is expanded to bring more satisfaction, more happiness to the self. And this expansion propels the self into the future. The self is poor, empty, and isolated, and hopes for relief through some future experience. It knows that it is incomplete in the present and that its only hope lies in the future, in different, improved circumstances. So it creates the idea of continuity for its existence, and what it cannot live today it will live tomorrow. Thus, it must continue through time. It must access the past and plan for the future. The present, for the self, is a means of reliving the past and reaching the future. But surely, the future is no more tangible than the past. In truth it does not exist. You may wait for the arrival of peace, harmony, and happiness in your life, but the present confusion and suffering are your reality. If you do not accept the present conflicts of your life as the reality of yourself, then certainly no future circumstance will ever free you.

The substance of the self—these basic qualities of separateness, continuity, and expansion—resists clarification and appears as inconstant as our thoughts, which wander perpetually from one triviality to another. Can such a self have any real continuity? Can it become something greater, something more perfect, something other than what it is? Can it exist as an entity separate from the world? These are fundamental questions that must be asked by anyone interested in living, for if the nature of our own self is not of interest to us, then we are not living at all.

To find the answers to these questions, we first must understand our entire process of thinking, for it is clear that the self is intimately involved in our thought process and with our memory.

Chapter 5

Thought and Self

W hat happens when we think? What part does memory play in the thought process? And who is the thinker, the one who remembers?

If you observe the process of thinking, you will first notice that the self classifies thoughts as belonging to the realm of "not me." The self appears to be the thinker, but the thought is separate. The self observes the thought, acts on the thought or not, judges the thought, or files the thought away for future reference. But, for the self, the thought is not the sense of "I." The thought is a result of something the *thinker*, the "I," has *done*. The thinker thinks; the thought is the result. The thinker considers the thought to be the same as any other creation of the self. The self causes it, but it is separate from the self. Therefore, for the self, the thought cannot be "me," assuming that the "me" is the thinker. Let's assume for the moment that the self is indeed the thinker, and follow this assumption through to its conclusion.

When we relive a powerful experience, what happens? Let's choose, for example, a sexual experience. We recreate, in our heads, the environment, the room, the bed, the lit candles—whatever was there. And we recreate the image of our partner. We imagine the touch, the smell, the sensations. We may even replay the dialogue—the sweet nothings and whispered promises. And in that re-creation we feel the emotions and imagined sensations. We play out, in our mind, our actions, responses, and words. And for that moment we are actually living inside this creation of our mind. Our consciousness exists inside this creation. Our sense of self is

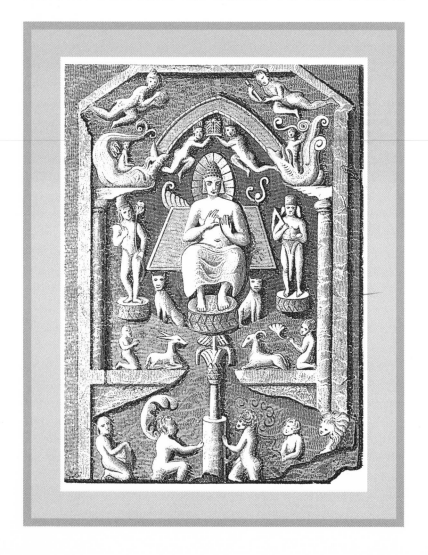

operating in the fantasy. We *feel* we are there—our *selves* are there. Our identity, the "I," exists in fullness and consciousness inside this image.

But this creation is a thought, or series of thoughts—images created by the mind. It is a scenario composed entirely of thoughts. How can our sense of self, our identity, our consciousness, even momentarily exist entirely inside a thought? Do we first build the thought, as we might build a house, and then move into it? Do we take only a piece of ourselves and lend it to the thought, bringing it back into ourselves when the thought is finished? If we are the thinker, then thought, which is our creation and therefore separate from us, cannot contain us. Yet we are contained by our thoughts a thousand times a day. Being "lost in thought" is a national pastime. Every daydream contains the self. Every imaginary wish and fantasy is nothing more than a temporary world in which the self lives.

If our sense of identity is contained in thought, even momentarily, then our *selves* cannot be the thinker. This revelation means either that something other than our self is the thinker, or that the thinker does not exist—instead only the process of thinking exists. In either case, if we are not the thinker, then what are we? For the thinker is clearly the chooser, the decider, the actor in life (if there is a reality to any of these things). If we are not the actor, not the chooser, not the doer, then what is left of the self?

We have pursued the line of separation between the self and the world and have pushed it back to the point where nothing whatsoever appears on the side of the "me," and all of existence appears to be the "not me." We have reached a logical absurdity, a fundamental contradiction. The self is all-important and immeasurably huge to itself, yet when it looks in the mirror, it sees a vacant hole. The self believes it-self to be the actor and chooser in life, and yet appears to have no power of choice or action. It is from this contradiction that all contradictions arise.

We must answer the question "who are we?" in order to dissolve this contradiction.

Chapter 6

We Are the World

The world of humankind is a creation of thought. Our institutions, our industry, our scientific progress have all been created by thought. Thought creates conflicting ideologies, and therefore wars and hostility. Thought creates social structures, customs, and collective habits, and therefore causes cultural separation and prejudice.

Thought created the concept of ownership. It created laws, politics, and national pride. It invented money. It created fashion, the trappings of wealth, and the concept of social status. It created our language and means of communication. And while thought did not create the reality of God, whatever that may be, it certainly created all of our concepts and ideas about God. It created all systems of religion: the dogmas, rituals, practices, and separative beliefs.

And thought created our selves. We are a product of thinking. Our very consciousness is grounded in the memories of all our past experiences, and this memory is the basis of thinking. We think in words or images, and these words and images have been acquired in memory through the action of experience.

We live in a world of thought, created by thought, and maintained by the process of thinking. And we ourselves are a product of thought. Our acquired prejudices, our beliefs, our manners, and our customs were given to us through a legacy of past thoughts handed down through generations. Our concepts of right and wrong, good and bad, have been created and refined by thought through thousands of years of internal struggles. The concepts of ambition, growth, acquisition, and generosity have existed as thoughts for as long as we have recorded time, and these thoughts continue through us. The process of thinking controls all of our actions, choices, and identifications. Our very consciousness would have no basis without memory, from which thinking gets its substance.

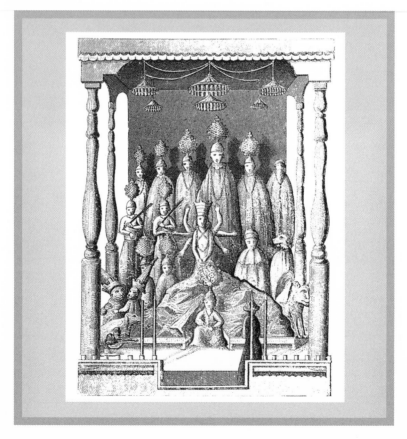

So our individuality, our consciousness, is a product of uncountable thoughts extending backward into the mists of time. The world has handed us a structure of thinking—intact—with which we identify and clothe ourselves. We are given the words, the concepts, the values, and to these we add what pitiful few experiences we have—and that is what we call our self.

Are we not then, in our fundamental form and nature, a product of the world in which we live? We feel, hope, fear, and dream like everyone else. All of our actions are motivated by the same greeds and desires as our neighbors, our friends, or our enemies. We feel the same pain, the same sense of loss, the same joy at the sight of beauty. Our thoughts and feelings originate from the same consciousness—the thought structure created through the world's evolution.

We are the world. Not as some warm, fuzzy image, nor as an intellectual concept, but in actuality, in form and substance, in truth. No line separates you from the world. There is no division, no wall. No entity exists to observe the "not me" from a position of separateness. Your very consciousness, your thoughts, your ambitions, your values, your striving—all of these are the world. You are the world, and the world is you. It is an inescapable fact, a tangible reality.

And yet our actions deny this. We act from a center, from the self. We deny our unity with the world and attempt to isolate and confine ourselves into a space outside of the world, a space that is "ours," in which we are in command. We want to exist in this space, to act and choose, to grow and become. We want to create within this space, to become mini-gods with true self-importance. We want continuance and immortality in this tiny space divided from the world.

I don't get this part ...

But no such space exists. We cannot separate ourselves from what we are.

We have attempted to separate ourselves from the world and create our own reality. And this attempt at separation has created conflict, as it must, because our false creation is opposed to its true self. From this conflict comes all suffering. We strive for beauty, yet we create ugliness. We yearn for truth, for God, for ultimate reality, but we have separated ourselves from these things; we have denied them. We want immortality, but immortality lies on the other side of the line that we (ourselves) have drawn.

The line that separates the self from the world is an illusion, a construct, a creation of thought. It has no basis in reality. But to see this with the intellect alone is of no value. The self is cunning and quick to seize intellectual constructs for its own purposes. It gets neverending pleasure through appearing wise and knowledgeable, and the more profound the intellectual discourse, the more wise and knowledgeable the self becomes. It is a great danger.

If we want to truly and deeply change, if we want to end suffering and ignorance, if we want to know reality, truth, and beauty; then understanding beyond the intellect is required. We must grasp, with our whole being, with our hearts and minds, the truth of our relationship to the world. We must understand that truly we are the world; the world is us. We must see, deeply, that we are not separate, see the true pettiness of our self, and understand the cause of suffering and ignorance.

Reaching this level of understanding is not an easy task, and it requires enormous energy. It requires a body and mind in reasonable harmony and a style of life that does not drain us to the point of emptiness. It requires clarity of thought, unhindered by numbing chemicals. It requires openness and willingness.

The next section describes the internal structure of the self—the "I", the ego, our self-image. A sound understanding of this structure is necessary in order to create a rational, true relationship between this self and the world.

Part Two

The Fabric of the Self

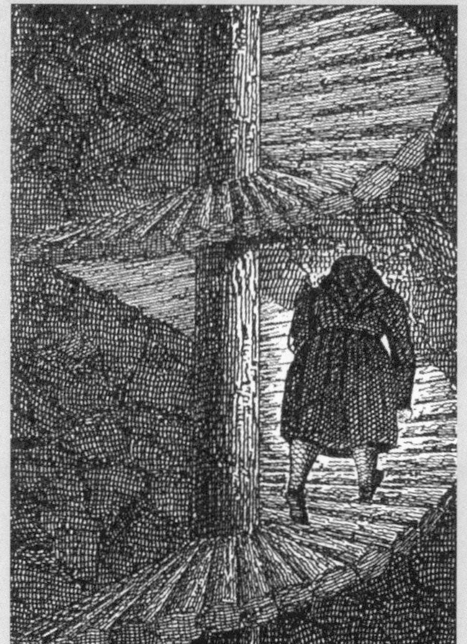

From the warp and weft of my experience, I shall weave the fabric of my life.

Traditional song of the Kogi Tribe of Columbia, sung while weaving

Chapter 7

Self-Perception

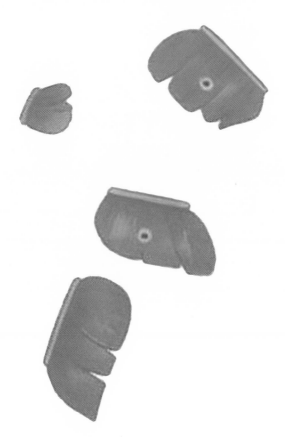

or truly alive - tor

When are we most acutely aware of ourselves? Isn't it when we are hurt? For example, if someone insults us we have a strong reaction. We feel wounded, angry, annoyed. The insult touches something deep within us, shakes some inner foundation. It is this inner thing that has been offended, that feels the hurt. But what is this thing?

Let's assume we consider ourselves to be charming, witty, and intelligent and someone else says or does something that implies we are dull. What actually happens? We are hurt; we feel damaged and offended. We are somehow affected by their attitude toward us. Yet our physical form is certainly not compromised, our mental capabilities not materially lessened. Our knowledge and memories remain intact; we do not change shape or form through another's words. We are no more or less charming, witty, and intelligent than before the insult was spoken. So what then suffers the hurt? What is it that feels damaged or threatened and responds with anger and resentment?

Whatever feels the insult must be susceptible to injury from the insult, or else there would be no hurt, no damage, and no resentful response. We can hurl verbal abuse at an inanimate object until we are blue in the face and the object, be it a wall, a rock, or a tree, will not respond. It is unaffected by words or whatever attitude we have toward it. We do not change or threaten it. But whatever it is inside us that feels an insult must be materially affected by that insult. It is wounded, which implies that words, ideas, and attitudes have caused a rupture in it, or at least the threat of rupture—for if words can threaten it, then it must believe itself susceptible to being damaged by words.

So what can possibly be damaged by words, by ideas, by images? It can only be an image itself. Certainly any image that we hold in our minds is susceptible to change, to expansion or shrinkage, to redefinition and reshaping. And what is it that reshapes an image in our minds? It can only be a thought—a series of words or ideas. Images are strengthened through complimentary ideas and weakened through

opposing ideas. We add and subtract things from our mental images according to a variety of whims. We have an image of our spouse at the time of first love or marriage; years later, the image that remains usually bears no resemblance to the original image. It has undergone the transformations of disappointment, frustration, boredom, and a long list of revelations. Moreover, these disappointments and frustrations are themselves created by other images—of our expectations, of what life would or should be like after marriage. So we have modified this image of our spouse through the action of ideas.

Images are highly susceptible to ideas, to words and concepts, to the actions and attitudes of other people. And our most endearing image is certainly our own self-image. We have created in our minds an image of ourselves, and this image is the thing that is affected by other people's opinions. Thus, it is the thing that is hurt when we are insulted.

We have formed conclusions about ourselves, and carefully constructed an image of who we are from these conclusions. We have concluded that we are intelligent or dull, handsome or unattractive, knowledgeable or ignorant. We have concluded that we have capabilities and talents in specific areas and that we can act in certain ways and achieve predictable results. We have created an image from these conclusions, and we rely on other people to validate our results. When they do not, the very foundations of our conclusions are threatened. We become hurt, angry, resentful, frightened. Our carefully constructed image is in danger of being damaged or even annihilated.

Any serious, earnest approach to the question "Who am I?" must begin with an understanding of this image of ourselves we have created. It is the source of our psychological hurts. It is the cause of our susceptibility to flattery. It creates, through comparison to other images, envy, jealousy, greed, fear, and a host of attachments and desires that are the root cause of our suffering. We must discover how we have created this self-image and whether we can move beyond it. We must find out for ourselves if anything more exists, and if it does, how we can come to it.

Chapter 8

The Creation of Our Self-Image

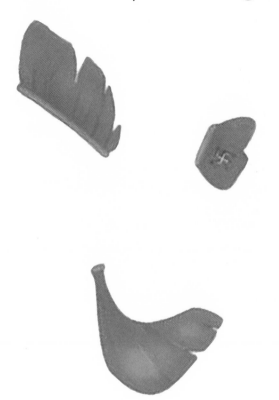

O ur self-image is not a fixed, static entity, something created in our distant past and rooted in the ground of stability and permanence. It is constantly changing, undergoing renovation or reconstruction. LD1 We are at every moment evaluating and refining this image. Insults to and assaults on the image cause hurt when they come from people we respect, and this hurt motivates us to reevaluate the image and perhaps remove or change certain features. Flattery from anyone reinforces aspects of our image. We add to or expand the sense of ourselves as intelligent or desirable and feel justified in our creation. Thus we use the world's adulations and offenses as motivators of change. Disapproval tends to diminish the image; approval enlarges it. But the real motivator of change is our own judgment, our own authority.

Whatever image we may have created for ourselves, it is generally insufficient. We want to make it more, better, stronger. We see flaws and faults that need repair or removal. We compare our image to the images we have of other people, and we find our own lacking. The insufficiency of our self-image is a cause of anxiety; it creates a sense of emptiness, of incompleteness, and we seek to shore up this image in order to escape these feelings. Thus we are perpetually engaged in rebuilding the image.

Our self-image is insufficient, incomplete as judged by our internal feelings, but when we attempt to make the image complete we are confronted by reality as it is manifest in our external relationships with the world. When we expand our self-image to eradicate all flaws, then we are assaulted by attitudes and actions from other people that deny, contradict, or obliterate our creation. The resulting hurt and insecurity motivate further modifications to our image in an unending spiral. An image of ourselves as compassionate and loving, for example, must face the reality of our pettiness and greed as revealed in the reflections of our relationships. People will respond to the reality of our pettiness, not our imagined compassion. We cannot ignore the gap between image and reality. Yet the harder we try to create the perfect image, the wider the gap will be. We are thus forever in conflict: our self-image struggling against the truth of ourselves.

We are hurt when someone insults us—our self-image is hurt. We also suffer self-inflicted hurts, caused by our own comparisons and critical judgments of our self-image. Our judgments, authority, and critical perceptions cause incessant injuries. And each assault creates a backlash of frantic redesign. We see that the image is insufficient, yet if we are sane and even moderately observant, we realize that reality cannot support a more perfect image. We resort to all manner of deceptions, deceiving both ourselves and those around us in an effort to create some reality in which our self-image can be supported.

Thus we begin a process of performing life rather than living life. We see that we are petty, envious, and fearful, but we strive for a self-image that is the opposite. So we begin to act the image of ourselves instead of our reality. We hold our pettiness in check and act graciously. We hide fearfulness and

act out courage. We disguise our insecurities and play the part of self-sufficiency. And we play the part so well that we deceive ourselves. We become players on the stage of life, acting out our self-created scripts. There is little reality to us, and therefore to the life we are playing.

The play is based on a lie, but the reality of ourselves cannot be perpetually kept in check. When our internal reality surfaces, it creates conflict and suffering because it is in opposition to the self-image that we are acting. We may pretend, for example, to be untouched by animal lusts, but the truth of our desires will constantly assault our image of indifference.

This conflict between our self-image and the reality of ourselves is the source of many psychological fears. One unwavering fear is that our deceptions will unravel and the image we have so carefully crafted will collapse. If, for example, we are greedy and self-centered and we believe ourselves to be generous and selfless, then situations that offer opportunities for self-indulgence create anxieties. We must be watchful lest we slip and let our real selves emerge.

Other fears arise from the false association of our self-image with external things. In an effort to bolster the image, we include every imaginable association. We add political affiliations, national and cultural memberships, social status. And what can be added can also be lost. Thus, we fear the loss of property and income because our self-image is closely identified with wealth and power, or we fear the loss of social status because our self-image includes titles, position, and respect from others.

In reality, our self-image is a heavy burden. We carry it around, nourish it, and maintain it. We lavish attention on it. We are constantly concerned with its welfare, and in return it is the cause of our conflicts, fears, and suffering. We might ask, "What is the point?" and indeed that is an intriguing question. But a more pressing question is, "What are the mechanisms that mold this self-image?" We need to discover its form and makeup, its inherent fabric—but we can learn little about this image until we know the mechanism by which it is made.

Chapter 9

The Forces of Change

Our self-image is a network of personal idiosyncrasies—our own variations on the themes of ambitions, sorrows, anxieties, beliefs, aspirations, opinions, and all the host of petty vanities with which we clothe ourselves. They are the characteristics of our temperament, the shadings of our character and personality.

From our conclusions about life we create our system of beliefs—our attitudes, values, and principles. They are fundamental to everything else in our self-image. They form our ideology: our image of what life, and ourselves, *should* be like. From these values we structure our rituals and traditions, create our habits and routines. They are the basis of our personal drive. All of our ambitions and the measurement of our achievements stem from these values, as do our rationalizations and justifications of failures and limitations.

Our virtues are rooted in these values, and because every virtue creates its own opposite, our vices likewise find a home there. This is the source of conflict. The struggle to maintain our principles and beliefs—our ideals—is the source of fear and anxiety. It is unavoidable. We are filled with neuroticisms, concerns, suppressions, and insecurities, and these fears are the root of our personal idiosyncrasies. They mold our temperament. They fuel our particular brand of sorrows, grief, and tears. They are the source of our

regrets, our bitterness, and our loneliness. They build up our burdens and manufacture our confusions. They are the source of our angers, our violence and brutalities, our dependence and desires. Even our passions and pleasures are rooted in fear, for if we look closely, we see that they are a reaction to fear. They are an escape.

Our self-image is a collection of beliefs, formed from our conclusions and woven together by fear. It is this fear that creates the structure of our self-image, and it is the motivator for change in the image.

If we observe carefully we see that an ideal exists for each aspect of our self-image, and that ideal is either an image of a specific individual or a composite of many people. We may, for example, admire a great humanitarian or artist, or perhaps a political or religious leader. From this admiration, we construct an ideal image of compassion, leadership, or creativity. This image becomes the standard against which we compare our own self-image, and we attempt to modify our self-image to emulate the ideal. Likewise, scorn or disrespect elicits an internal image, an ideal, of greed, vileness, or cruelty. We compare our self-image to this negative ideal and attempt to move as far from it as we can.

When we create the ideal, we move the process of image creation to a new level of abstraction. We may have an internal image of our spouse or partner, and while that image may be warped and twisted beyond recognition, it nevertheless has a correspondence, however tenuous, with the reality of the person. In fact, a person does exist corresponding to the image we have created. But can we say the same of our ideal images? Clearly not. The ideal has no corresponding reality. It is a fabrication based on our conclusions of what people *could* or *should* be, or how they *might* behave. Yet we treat these ideals as if they were as tangible as the floor under our feet.

It is these ideal images—formed from cultural icons, from stories told to us by parents, from legend and fairy tale, from newsreels and magazines, from schooling, and from our own experience—that shape our self-image. We create in our minds an ideal image, based originally on what we have seen

or heard of other people, and that ideal in turn creates our
self-image.

Our self-image is in reality a reaction to the sum of our
ideals. We manufacture the image of the ideal, then attempt
to mold our self-image to match it. As the self-image reacts to
our changing ideals, the gap between the image and the reality widens. It is then shaped in the opposite direction due to
the conflict thus created, and we react by modifying the ideal
to something that we hope we can achieve. These two opposing reactions—the attraction of the ideal and the intrusion of
perceived reality as seen in our relationship to the world—
are the forces that mold our self-image. Each is based on
comparison. And comparison, in turn, is driven by fear.

Chapter 10

The Relationship Between Images

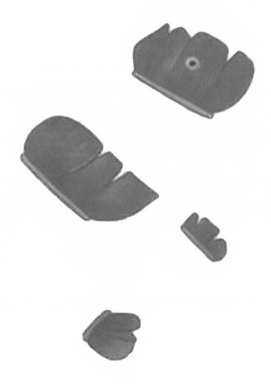

We have seen that we are able to modify the image that we have of ourselves, and in fact we are almost constantly engaged in doing so. We are able to expand the image, add elements to it, subtract elements from it, or completely reshape certain aspects. If we have just received a promotion at work, our new self-image includes an improved title, position, sense of power, and so forth. We see ourselves as somehow different than we were before the promotion. Our improved position implies greater security and therefore less fear. Our self-image has been expanded. This change was brought about by comparison; all such changes in our self-image result from the process of comparison.

We each, for example, have an image of our mental capacities. We consider ourselves to be intelligent or stupid or somewhere in between. This image of our mental capacity exists only in relationship to our internal images of other people: it tells us how we rate on a relative scale. There can be no "smart" or "stupid" quality of our self-image without images of other people, for what does "stupid" mean in the absence of comparison? It is a term which inherently implies the existence of its opposite, so if we have an image of ourselves as "stupid," then somewhere within us there exists an image of someone else who is "not stupid." In school we are told one thing or another about our intelligence. Our parents reinforce it. We score above average or below average on our tests. We have created an internal scale of intelligence, and we rate ourselves according to this scale.

So we compare our mental capacities with those around us. Circumstances that flatter our intellects give us a feeling of mental superiority, and we move the scale ever so slightly in the positive direction. In opposite circumstances, we feel inferior and slightly shift our scale back.

This process holds true for all aspects of our self-image. Our images as wealthy or poor, powerful or weak, talented or

not, require a scale of comparison. Even our self-images as
engineers, doctors, parents, spiritual aspirants and the like
take on meaning only in comparison. We feel that being an
engineer is more or less desirable than being a clerk, or
being a parent is superior to being childless—each of which
is an internal image with which we compare ourselves.

As we begin to delve into the structure of our self-image,
we find that the attributes of our self-image appear to be intimately connected to our internal images of other people—
either specific individuals or generic categories of people.
We compare, and this comparison is the defining quality of
our self-image.

Our self-image cannot exist in the absence of our internal
images of others. It is a network of comparisons, and comparison has no meaning without the "other." Our image of another is simply one point on a scale that is a structural
component of our self-image. That image is, in reality, an in-
tegral part of our self-image.

It is the image itself that is important to us. It is the image that motivates us to action. Even tangible events, such as
a job promotion, are relevant only to the degree that our image of the event includes increased status, self-importance,
or power.

We compare ourselves to the sum total of the images we
hold of our partners, neighbors, friends, coworkers, and
bosses—all of our relationships with the world. And these
images are not the reality. Our spouses or partners have,
more than likely, changed little in any substantial, fundamental way since we first met them and fell in love. Yet our perceptions of them have likely changed radically. The image
that we currently have of them may resemble our original
image only superficially. The original image caused our initial

desire to bond with them, and the current image may now be causing regret.

Because all internal images are intimately connected to our self-image, we must look closely at our images of others—how they are created and transformed—in order to come to the root of our own self-image.

Chapter 11

The Projection of Self-Image

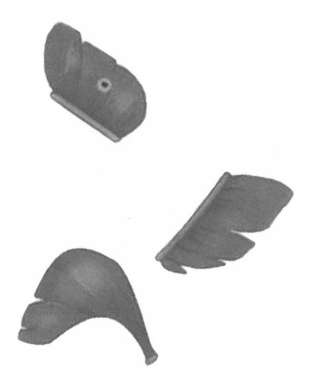

*O*ur self-image is inflated beyond any semblance of reality by the influence of our ideals, and the qualities of our self-image created by these ideals in turn mold the images we have of others. If we have an image of ourselves as being eloquent and charming, then we interpret politeness in others as interest in ourselves. Someone may listen to our dialogue with an intent look and a smile while hoping we will soon shut up, yet we perceive the attention as evidence of our irresistible charisma. We form an image of that person as someone who is truly interested in us, and we feel warmth toward that image. If we have an image of ourselves as sexually desirable, even irresistible, then we will interpret even a glance from someone who interests us as a look of desire. We ascribe hidden meanings to their words and form an image of them as possible sexual partners. If we are proud, then we imagine that others admire us and we hear flattery as sincerity. If we believe ourselves to be a great guru or teacher, we see devotion and awe in those around us. If we are paranoid, we find hostility and threat in people's actions and form images of them as menacing and aggressive.

Thus we interpret the actions and words of those around us according to the self-image we have constructed. We do this because others' actions and words have significance to us

only to the extent that they affect us. We are self-centered; our concern is only for ourselves. We are interested in how people treat us, think of us; whether they stay with us or leave us; whether they love us or hate us; whether they comfort us, support us, entertain us; whether they keep us from being lonely or isolated. We want companionship, friendship, love, respect, and admiration, and we seek to avoid animosity and bitterness.

We want comfort and security from the people around us. But it is our self-image that seeks the security. As we saw in the first chapter, when we are hurt by insults or disrespectful attitudes it is really our self-image that is hurt. In the same manner it is our self-image that is insecure. In an effort to achieve security, it projects itself onto others, forming images of them that support its own structures. Thus we never relate to people as they are. We relate instead to the images of them that the needs of our own self-image have created.

We are insecure in our self-image; this must be the case because our self-image cannot be supported by reality. It is molded by ideals, by how things *might* be, by how we *should* behave and feel, and this molding is in constant conflict with our true natures. To support this unreal structure, our self-image projects itself onto others and creates correspondingly unreal images of them. These images are created by our self-image in its own image. They are extensions of itself. They are in fact an inseparable part of our self-image. Without these artificial images of others, our self-image would collapse. They are a bulwark against the intrusion of reality, and they allow us to continue our incessant march toward the ideals we have created for ourselves.

So our self-image consists of a core of ideals, aspirations, and ambitions that mold our opinions and beliefs, our fears and insecurities, our desires and habits. Our entire repertoire of vanities, arrogance, regrets, and hopes resides in this core. And from this core radiate images of others, as limbs from a body, that provide the support required to maintain our self-image. This is the structure of our self-image. It is the structure of ourselves. It is an exercise in vanity, resulting in an unreal world in which we live out our sorrowful existence.

Surely, such delusion is not what you intended long ago, from the vantage point of that small child you once inhabited, when you looked at the vast unknown of life and with awesome anticipation imagined your life as an adult. You surely could not have imagined the self-created isolation and loneliness brought about by the absurdity of your self-image. Nevertheless, can you, after years of careful cultivation of these absurdities, heal this image? Can it be brought into line with the reality of yourself? Can it be healed entirely, made whole, made complete? I say with certainty: Yes.

It is an absolute necessity that we heal this image of ourselves—not partially, in pieces here and there, but completely, in its totality. We must make the image whole. It

must correspond precisely with the reality of ourselves. If we are able do that, then all our images of others will evaporate; we will no longer need to buttress our self-image with artificial images of others. We will relate to people as they are, in their reality, from our own position of reality.

This realignment can be achieved. It is not mere theory or philosophy. Nor is it an opinion or a belief. It is a reality, a fact, and this fact can be experienced by anyone who wishes to look into it. It is within the reach of everyone.

Chapter 12

Change

W e have seen how self-image is formed and how it changes. We have looked at its structure and its operation. And we have seen that comparison is the driving force that creates and maintains the image. We must find out, fundamentally, at its very source, why we compare. Comparison is necessary at some level. We must compare prices, schools, clothes—these comparisons are essential and our minds are appropriately structured to perform such comparisons. But why do we compare ourselves to other people or to ideals? Why do we compare ourselves to anything at all? Comparison is necessary for choice, and we

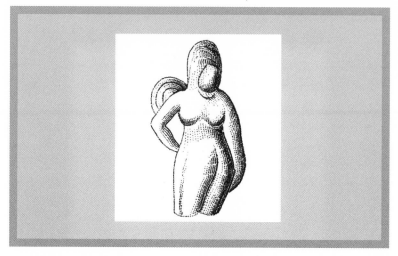

choose between various goods and services, between different types of cars or watches, between living in the mountains
or by the ocean. But when we compare our selves to something, then where is the choice? We are what we are. We cannot make a self-comparison and then simply choose to be
something or someone else based on the outcome of the
comparison. It's an absurdity. Yet we compare ourselves to
everyone and to every ideal at every opportunity.

We compare because we assume, at some level, that we
can become something different, something other than what
we are, through the process of effort and time. But is this assumption true? Does it have any basis in fact? Can we alter
our basic natures, our drives and fears, our loneliness and
sorrows through the action of time? Clearly we can become
more or less wealthy, more or less knowledgeable, or more or
less talented through time. We can collect possessions,
change partners, and rise up the corporate ladder. We can
become involved in religions and gain spiritual knowledge,
but does any of this change who we are? Does any of this
modify our basic need for attachments? Does it extinguish
the source of our desires or change our deep prejudices?
Does it transform our violence into love, or our vanities into
humility? It does not. Whatever we may attempt to change
within us, through the process of comparison or through
effort, will become stronger. We will create its opposite
within us and we will begin again the unending conflict of
our ideals against our realities.

True change—lasting, fundamental change—can only
take place now, in the moment. It is not of the will, or of
time. It cannot happen tomorrow, and it cannot take place
gradually, step by step—adding a little here and removing a

little there. This is the process we have been employed in for
most of our lives—gradually building our self-image and de-
constructing it to meet the demands of our ideals, the demands of the future. We have been living for the future,
trying to change for the future. But this is futile. This process
has led us to our current state. We are empty and we have
created a world of emptiness, a world of wars, prejudice, and
hatreds. A world based on greed and possessiveness, on acquisition and self-centeredness. Can we not see the futility of
our actions—the futility of change through comparison?

Change through comparison implies a goal, something
we are growing toward. But this goal is an ideal—a creation

of our minds, based on the existing insufficiency of ourselves. It has no basis in reality. It is a hope, a dream, an artificial construct. It can never be reached, and any attempt to reach it will create conflict. We are who we are, and this cannot be changed until we stop running from this reality of ourselves. We must stop escaping from ourselves through the quest for the ideal. We turn on backs on our true natures each time we try to change them. We glimpse our insufficiencies and immediately struggle against them. We judge ourselves. The act of comparing denies the substance of our natures. It implies that our natures are insubstantial and subject to change through whim. I assure you; they are not. Anger or lust cannot be ripped from ourselves through any action of force, will, or wanting. It is anger that seeks to remove anger. We are angry that we have anger and we must rid ourselves of it. And as we pour our energy into the task of removing anger, we pour that energy into anger itself. We strengthen it, solidify it, and deepen its roots.

Change can only happen if we remove the ideal, if we eradicate our goals and end the process of comparison. When we do this, we are left with ourselves, as we are. It is in the act of observation itself, without choice or judgment, that change occurs. The awareness of ourselves as we are—naked, devoid of images and free from comparison—is the force of true change. It is in awareness that love blossoms. It is the beginning of compassion and the unfolding of beauty.

We must divest ourselves of the absurdities of our self-image. We must stop the process of comparison. We must abandon our ideals. We must see ourselves, wholly, with full heart and mind, as we are. Only then can we heal ourselves. We can only do this with a clear body and mind. Self-awareness requires enormous energy. If we are wasting energy in large quantities, or not restoring our energies through rational living, then the task is insurmountable. We cannot come to the truth of ourselves if we cannot reason, if we are sluggish or unbalanced, or if our attention is scattered. Our bodies must be in a state of real health, our minds must be clear, and we must be alert and balanced. The remainder of this book addresses these issues and provides guideposts for those persons willing to proceed.

Part Three

❋

Relational Yoga

If the doors of perception were cleansed, everything would appear to man as it is—infinite.

William Blake

Chapter 13

The Path of Yoga

Yoga, like all things suffering the onslaughts of time and tradition, has become divided into different schools, different practices, different beliefs. Each school of thought has adherents who scorn the opposition and promote the truth of their own way. Each has its own ritualistic approach to the science of yoga, and each can neatly explain the reasons for and necessity of its own idiosyncrasies. This is as it should be; it is the natural course of the evolution of thought.

If we step back even slightly in time, however, we find that the different yogas, with a few exceptions, have a common source. Almost all yoga practiced in the world today can be traced to one of four masters of the art. The various forms of Ashtanga, or power yoga, can all be traced to Patabhi Jois, who began teaching in the early 1950s. B.K.S. Iyengar founded Iyengar yoga, the largest school of yoga existing today. Most yoga schools stressing static hatha yoga postures owe their existence in some measure to Iyengar. T.K.V. Desikachar founded Viniyoga (in India simply called yoga), and Indra Devi is the source of nearly every system of yoga in Latin America. Each of these four masters in turn learned from a common source: T. Krishnamacharia. They were each his disciples.

There are a few exceptions. The school of Kriya yoga owes its existence, according to its adherents, to an immortal saint called Babaji Nagaraj. According to legend, Babaji has lived for over a thousand years. In the middle 1800s Babaji taught yoga to Lahiri Mahasaya, who taught Sri Yukteswar, who in turn taught Paramahansa Yogananda. It was Yogananda who brought Kriya yoga to America in the early 1900s. After Yogananda revealed the existence of Babaji, he appeared to hundreds of others, passing on his

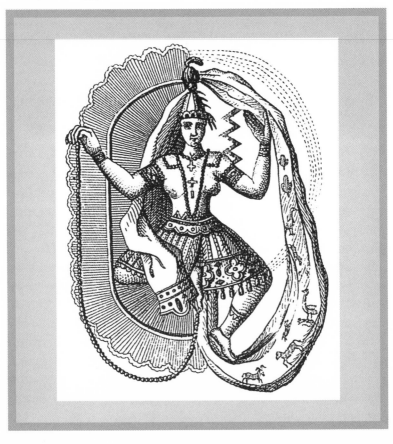

yoga secrets and instructing the chosen to go out and teach the world. These appearances spawned the multitude of Kundalini and Kriya yoga sects that dot the world today. Whether Babaji exists outside the imaginations of those whom he visited is really of no importance, for we know that Yogananda, Sri Yukteswar, and Lahiri Mahasaya did exist, and that Yogananda, at least, possessed an art that helped create harmony between body and mind.

Another exception is Bikram yoga, the newest yoga rage sweeping the country from its source in Hollywood. Bikram yoga is performed in a heated room and uses a fixed number of postures that are nearly identical to a subset of Iyengar postures. It was founded by Bikram Choudhury.

If we focus on the differences between these various yoga systems, or get caught up in the narrowness of one school or another, then we are missing the true value of yoga. If only for justification for their existence, all systems of yoga ultimately revert back to the original source: the Yoga Sutras of Patanjali.

Patanjali lived and wrote approximately two thousand years ago. He wrote the Yoga Sutras in a cryptic, sometimes enigmatic style; the reader gets the impression that he was hurriedly jotting down notes to himself about life as it was happening to him, or writing while he was otherwise engaged. It would be a wonder that such a tiny book—in an ancient language, referring to events and concepts that no longer exist, with a style that is difficult to read and even more difficult to understand—could survive the millennia, undergo uncountable translations and found a worldwide tradition, were it not for the work's razor-sharp insights. These glimpses of reality slice through the intellect and for a brief moment illuminate something unknown.

That Patanjali possessed profound insights into the human condition is without question. What might be questioned is whether these insights can be transmitted to another. If reality is yourself, your basic nature, as he believed, it is within each of us. Can anyone show you that? Who can read to you the book that is written in your own thoughts, in your own actions, in your own web of desires and fears? This is the problem that Patanjali faced and knew too well. And yet he wrote and had an audience.

The Sutras of Patanjali are not a bus to take you anywhere. They are a collection of road signs. Patanjali points, incessantly, in the same direction—inward. At each twist and turn we seek something from him, and he points back at us. The science of yoga, as laid out by Patanjali, is a set of tools for constructing a mirror in which we can see our selves clearly. This is the end result of yoga—its purpose, its value, its intent.

In Sutra I.30, Patanjali states some of the main obstacles to self-awareness: bodily sickness, inability to reason, sluggishness, lack of balance or moderation, scattered attention. Self-awareness requires enormous energy. If we are wasting energy in large quantities, or not restoring our energy through rational living, then the task is insurmountable. The value of yoga is that it brings the body to a state of real health, clarifies the mind, transforms sluggishness and laziness into a state of alertness, and moves us into a state of balance. From this state only can we clearly and fearlessly gaze into the void of our selves.

It does not matter which yoga system we choose to follow. What matters is the attitude with which we approach the process. If we have perceived the true value of yoga, then our attitudes are already properly focused. All we need is a brief description of the existing tools of yoga and how they are used to construct the mirror of the self.

Chapter 14

The Body

*E*very day I speak with someone who professes to be on the path to self-knowledge and yet, at the same time, is numbing their brain with alcohol or drugs, or immersing themselves in non-stop entertainments or other sensory overloads. Or their lives consist entirely of sedentary activities, punctuated by trips to the office or the grocery store. Or they overeat to the point of ill health. This aspect of the powers of delusion within our self-image is astonishing. We deceive ourselves into believing that we are attempting to know ourselves while we simultaneously cripple our instrument of awareness—our body. It is such an obvious impossibility, and yet we consistently delude ourselves.

The next time you attend a cocktail party, try this experiment: refrain from drinking. Watch the people around you and pay attention to the conversation. At the beginning everyone will sound their usual sober eloquence, but as the evening wears on you will notice a gradual and determined deterioration in the quality and coherence of discourse. The participants will not notice and will, in fact, believe themselves to be in top form. Not everyone will deteriorate at the same rate. If enough people are present, some few may rapidly devolve beyond pre-schooling. Their speech will become incoherent and they will forget how to walk, perform normal bodily functions, and even recognize their surroundings. They will have lost 100% of their intelligence. Some others will merely become curiously slow thinking and will display repetitive speech patterns and limited cognitive functioning. Do not delude yourself into thinking that there is some fine line between the person who devolves to the point of losing all cognitive ability and the person who only takes a few drinks and feels fine—that you maintain full intelligence up to a point and then, after one too many, slide precipitously into senselessness. There is a perceptible and cumulative loss of intelligence with each sip of alcohol. There are no exceptions. It is a fun thing to watch if you are sober and doing it for the first time. But try to imagine that any of the people you are watching are engaged in a serious attempt to know themselves. You will be forced to laugh.

I'm not saying it is either right or wrong to consume alcohol in any quantity whatsoever. There is no moral component to the act. Nor is there a moral component to taking drugs, overeating, or doing anything that you wish with your own body. Please, indulge if you want. Have at it. You are all adults. However, doesn't it seem foolish to embark on a journey that requires our full mental capacity and at the same time to cripple that capacity beyond any hope of its utility? If we wish to drink, take drugs, or otherwise incapacitate the body, then we should not delude ourselves into thinking that we are seriously on the path to truth. We may be on the path, but we are certainly not serious. And seriousness is a prerequisite to this process.

Why do we drink or take mind-altering drugs? Why do we immerse ourselves in non-stop entertainments, or use food as a sedative, or allow our bodies to become weak, stiff, and nearly useless through sedentary living? We drink or take recreational drugs because they numb our minds or our bodies or both. We may subjectively feel that drugs have expanded our consciousness, or opened up a new level of perception, but in reality they have closed off our anxieties and artificially colored our vanities and arrogance. They allow us to escape from our inner loneliness or pain or fear. We may have inner insecurities and find ourselves unable to communicate openly, so we take a drink at parties in order to numb that insecurity and we find ourselves more talkative or social. But what have we done in this process? We have escaped the very thing that we must approach. Our insecurity is the symptom that we must observe, study, and embrace in order to discover the deeper cause that can lead us to ourselves.

The same holds true for overeating or seeking non-stop entertainments. We attempt to fill some inner emptiness with food, or we escape from the reality of the moment by immersing ourselves in video games, television, on-line browsing, shopping, or anything else that can keep the nagging uncertainties of ourselves at bay.

And why do we pursue inactive lifestyles? Why do we create rigidity and weakness in bodies that need flexibility and strength in order to function in their natural state? We sleep, wake, go to the office, sit at our desks, return home, sit in front of the TV, eat, and sleep. We intersperse a few hours of golf or an occasional trip to the gym and we call all of this living. We are motivated to dull our bodies because in doing so we correspondingly dull the mind. We create a further escape from the tension of our inner beings. When we make an effort to bring the body back to full capacity and health, we experience pain, both physical from the process of movement, and emotional from the increased awareness that accompanies the increased alertness of the body. So we move inexorably in the direction of a sedentary life, filled with entertainments and mind-numbing sensory experiences.

If we are serious about the process of self-discovery, then we must acknowledge that the body is the instrument of perception. We must acknowledge that our brain is the instrument of thought and reason, and that the brain is also part of the body. Can we conceivably reach a full understanding of ourselves if we disregard the capacities and needs of our bodies?

The first step in any serious enquiry into ourselves that can lead to a fundamental healing, must be an enquiry into the state of our bodies. I think that most of you will find that the body needs to be freed from the prison of mind-numbing substances, mindless entertainments, or sedentary living to which it has been sentenced by the absurdities of our self-image and our twisted relationship to the world.

Chapter 15

The Breath

As we have neglected our bodies and used them for entertainment or sensual purposes, we have likewise co-opted our breath from its natural connection with the body and have made it a tool of our self-image—a tool of our emotional state. We allow our fears, pleasures, excitements, and sorrows to take over our breathing whenever convenient. We use the breath as we use drugs—to dull our sensibilities.

Nearly all yoga traditions, to some extent, stress the breath as a focus of attention. Patanjali writes, "Through the right control of breathing (Prana), we overcome ignorance" (I.52). Mystics and sages throughout history, from both Eastern and Western traditions, have claimed an intimate connection between breathing and consciousness; some even assert that breath *is* consciousness. If this approach seems overly mystical, then don't buy into it; it isn't important. It is obvious in any case that breathing occupies a unique position in human experience. It is the one constant bodily function that is autonomous (we breathe perfectly well while asleep or when our attention wanders), and yet we have full conscious control of it. It appears to exist at some boundary between our conscious existence and the unconscious. If we look at the broad process of living and dying, then the in-breath can be considered our first act in life, and exhaling is certainly

our last. Our lives are bounded by the breath, and in between birth and death we live within a constant circle of breathing. The connection between our breath and our emotional state is certainly evident. In fear, our breath is quick, pulsing, rapid-fire, and shallow. In anger it is ragged and fierce. In pain we breathe in fully and hold. In pleasure we breathe out fully and hold. In anticipation we breathe in halfway and hold. In contentment our breath is so slow, deep, and even as to be hardly perceptible. The breath is clearly connected to our emotional state, yet it is not clear that it is connected in the most supportive manner. Given all of this, the breath seems indeed to be something that we should delve into.

To use our breath as a proper tool for self-inquiry, however, we must first learn to breathe differently. One simple technique is called Ujjayi breathing. It has been around since Patanjali's time and is amazingly easy to learn. However, it is one of those maddeningly obtuse things, like learning to tie your shoelaces, that stubbornly resists verbal descriptions. For those who wish to attempt a verbal approach, appendix A provides one. For the rest, simply contact your nearest yoga center and find someone who will teach you, which I strongly recommend. It takes a few minutes and most should be happy to instruct you for free. All Viniyoga teachers rely heavily on Ujjayi breathing, as do most Ashtanga yoga centers. With Iyengar, Bikram, and Kriya it will be hit and miss, but usually you can find at least one teacher familiar with the technique.

Ujjayi is a method of breathing that ties the breath more closely to the conscious side of breathing. It blurs the line between conscious and unconscious activities. Once learned, you can quite easily engage in normal activities while maintaining a slightly greater conscious awareness of the breath. You may say, "So what?" but this conscious awareness is the beginning of a much deeper awareness that is your focus in knowing and understanding your self.

I am not saying that serious self-inquiry is impossible without knowledge of Ujjayi breathing. Such a statement would be patently absurd. All that is necessary to know your self is a burning desire to do so, and of course, clarity and energy. However, much of what follows in this book will be of little use to you without a comfortable knowledge of Ujjayi. Please, contact your nearest yoga center, get off the sofa, and learn it. I will assume from here on that we all know the Ujjayi breath.

As we have seen, the breath is intimately connected to our emotional state in terms of its rhythm, power, and evenness. Likewise, it is connected to our thoughts, and to our activities in and relationships with the world. And it is in our relationship to the world, through activity, that we wish to discover ourselves. Knowledge of your breath while sitting in the lotus pose, or while meditating on a mantra, a yantra, or even your navel, will do you little good. It is through relationship, through action, that the self expresses its nature and can be seen. Anyone can find peace in a cave, but bringing that peace into the chaos of the world is the issue. And it is necessary to find that peace within the world in order to know the true self, in order to discover your true relationship with the world.

Chapter 16

The Intellect

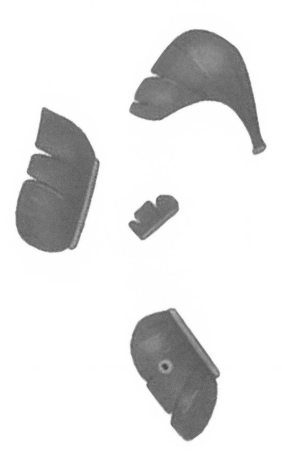

It is the intellect—the thought process—that creates our self-image. It is the intellect that is in control of much of our lives and of the world. Thought has created division, possessiveness, and ambition. It has created the world's dogmas and beliefs. It has created the world's pleasures—for pleasures are nothing more than sensation combined with thought.

Thought is divisive. It has divided the world into good and bad, useful and useless, the "me" and the "not me." It has created divisive religions, traditions, rituals, principles, and prejudices. And it has divided itself from our hearts. It has created an idea of "understanding" in which intellectual consistency equals true understanding. It assumes that we can build a concept, be it of the idea of "good" or the meaning of "marriage," and that we can understand the reality underlying this concept through the rational process of analyzing that concept. If a concept matches our experiences, is internally consistent, makes logical sense, and we can create a coherent internal image of it, then we "understand" it. We know the reality of it. But all we have done is create an image of the thing we wish to understand; something that may correspond to reality, but certainly is not reality. And the thing that we understand is this image—this self-created structure of thought. It is an intellectual understanding—incomplete, fragmented. It is not whole. It does not touch reality at any point. There is a deeper understanding that is possible. It is the understanding that blossoms when heart and mind are whole, as one. It is the understanding that happens when we are choicelessly present, in the moment, free from judgments and comparisons, which are the tools of the intellect.

The intellect certainly has its place in the process of self-discovery. Without the intellect we would never begin. We would not have words or communication. We would have no concepts of the world that we could share with others. It is the natural task of the intellect to grasp a structure, a concept that meaningfully describes the nature of ourselves. It is then the natural task of our full being to find the truth behind the words that the intellect has put together. For example, through reading this book we may have intellectually grasped the fact that we project our self-image onto others. We may have reasoned it through and we "agree" with the conclusion. But this agreement, in itself, is meaningless. It will have no validity in our lives until we begin to look for this process as it is happening in our daily lives—when we begin to question its validity through experimentation. We must "see" the process in action. We must experience and observe ourselves actually projecting our self-image as we interact with those around us. This is the true seeing.

Some people do, through facing extraordinary suffering or through a profound crisis from which they do not attempt to escape, come spontaneously to self-understanding and truth, and they heal themselves. But for most, we must first grasp, intellectually, the truth of ourselves in terms of concepts and verbal structures and then observe that truth through experimentation. The fact that, in this book, we chose "self-image" as an appropriate paradigm of ourselves is of no consequence. We could equally as well have chosen the composition of memory and thought, or the metaphor of "observer" and "observed." It is of no significance. In this book we did choose self-image as our paradigm, our metaphor, and it is an appropriate paradigm. The important factor of any paradigm is: does it accurately describe, in words, the truth of ourselves? Whatever metaphor we use, assuming it is accurate, it will provide the appropriate questions that our hearts and minds can jointly pursue. For example, since we have in our minds a structure that describes the workings of our self-image, then the question, among others, will inevitably arise—"Is it truly the self-image that is hurt when we are offended, or is it something else?" This is a stimulus for inquiry for both the heart and the intellect. The pursuit of the answer cannot be intellectual alone. Our full being must find the truth of it—through seeing ourselves in action—by observing our deeds, our thoughts, and our feelings. You must see the answer as you see the danger of a slippery precipice on which you are standing. Such a "seeing" is not of the intellect alone. Your entire being takes part. It is through questioning, with the burning desire to know the answer, that the truth is revealed. And it is ourselves whom we must question. This questioning of ourselves is the only road to a full healing of ourselves.

The danger of the intellect is that we can fall into the habit of "agreement" and then deceive ourselves. We agree or we disagree with statements or ideas, and we declare them as true or false. But neither agreement nor disagreement has any helpful importance. Agreement creates belief, an escape from the difficult process of discovery; while disagreement creates denial and it closes the doors to inquiry. Belief and denial are based on authority—either our own authority or the authority of others—and thus they are false securities, straws to which we cling. They are the death of discovery. They are goals, ends, and discovery is endless. Life is a constant movement and belief is a static image of life. They are incompatible.

The intellect seeks an end, a static finality of neat agreements that provides security, but such does not exist. We must instead use the intellect as a guidepost. It must be no more than a pointer to something that we must discover with our full beings, through the process of questioning and seeking answers through action—through relating in the moment to the world around us.

Chapter 17

The Process of Breathing

N ow that we know the Ujjayi breath and have become friends with it, we can begin putting it to use. Our first order of business is to integrate it into our yoga practice. For Viniyoga and Ashtanga students or teachers, who have already done this, please be patient—skip to the next chapter or amuse yourself with something more interesting while the rest of us plod on.

There are two reasons why we would want to integrate Ujjayi into our yoga practice. First, it is initially difficult, and thereby we gain the greatest mastery of it. It is like anything else that we learn: the more difficult the training, the quicker and more profound the mastery. It is the formula chosen by Olympic athletes, chess players, and anyone else who is serious about a subject. Second, the integration of Ujjayi into yoga postures begins the process of connecting the breath to the natural movement and conditions of the body, thereby disconnecting it from the frenzied conditions of our emotions—our fears, desires, angers, anticipations, emotional hurts, and varied pleasures. This is an important process in the quest for clarity. If our consciousness is blown about by the ever-shifting winds of our fears and desires, from that center of constant movement it will be difficult to find the stillness in which understanding blossoms.

The most important consideration in combining yoga postures with the Ujjayi breath is that the breath should remain constant throughout the practice. It is more important to continue breathing with the Ujjayi breath than to coordinate the in-and-out breaths with specific motions or positions of the body. The least resistant coordination will happen naturally when we reach the point where Ujjayi breathing becomes a simple and natural way to breathe during our yoga practices. But in the beginning, simply focus on continuing the Ujjayi breath and attempt to keep the breath even. This evenness will be difficult to achieve at first, especially during poses that we find uncomfortable or strenuous. Our tendency in such poses is to drop back into normal breathing and allow the breath to become raspy and labored (an impossibility if we maintain the Ujjayi breathing). After a few sessions however, if we pay attention, the breath will naturally remain with the Ujjayi at all times and will therefore remain smooth.

As you become more comfortable with the Ujjayi, you will find that your in-breaths naturally coordinate themselves with movements that expand the front of the body, such as moving into up dog, or cobra. Movements that compress the front of the body will coordinate themselves naturally, without conscious intent, with your exhalations, for example moving into Utanasana, or child's pose. You will also find that moving into positions that extend the arms or legs will naturally bring an in-breath, while those that contract the arms or legs will bring an exhalation. While we remain in a given pose, the breath will find its own rhythm, then transition naturally to the next pose. All this will be managed by the innate intelligence of the body and breath if you allow it. You will find no need for conscious control, as long as you maintain the continuity of the Ujjayi breath throughout the session.

You may at first have difficulty continuing the Ujjayi breath in inverted poses, such as sarvagasana (shoulder stand) or shirshasana (headstand). It may be difficult in these poses to maintain the Ujjayi sound, or the smoothness, or the seesaw movement, or all three, but stay with it and it will soon become easy and natural.

If we practice yoga with any regularity, a state of comfort with our breathing should occur in a few weeks' time. When we have thus mastered Ujjayi within the safe harbor of our yoga poses, we can begin to bring its effects into the world of our other relationships.

We should remind ourselves at this point that no amount or type of breathing will lead us to anything other than breath control. It will not reveal to us any transcendental truths or fundamental realities. It will not show us the nature

of ourselves or the workings of our thought processes. It will, however, remove certain physiological hindrances to perception and clarify our inner vision. We may then, if we possess sufficient courage, drive, determination, and energy, begin the task of actually looking at ourselves. The breathing is a pastime; the perception and understanding are the true work.

Chapter 18

Meditation and Self-Understanding

Meditation is one of the most over-used words in any spiritual vocabulary. It means different things to different people. It raises images of cross-legged saints sitting motionlessly in silence while performing some deep mysterious mental discipline, the purpose of which is only vaguely understood. Many of us have practiced meditation of various sorts—thinking a mantra, visualizing complex images, watching the breath, etc. Most of these techniques have as their goal the silencing of the thought process. None of these techniques is more or less effective than any other at bringing the meditator into a state of complete self-understanding, for in spite of strenuous arguments to the contrary, self- understanding is not the object of these techniques. We cannot seriously believe that by controlling and shutting down the thought process we will find, in such artificially created silence, a profound understanding of our complex inner structure and the interplay of deception, greed, ambition, fear, and all the rest. The concept is ridiculous. Anyone who has spent time seriously pursuing meditation will have discovered the futility of this goal, although indeed these types of meditation do offer other benefits. These techniques are simply tools that clear the path to perception so that the real work of self-observation and self-understanding can more easily commence.

If you have approached meditation with an attitude of serious inquiry, you will have discovered that these practices can create a profound quietness of the mind. But this quietness is usually confined to the place and time of meditation. After the meditation is finished and we return to the world of business, family, and responsibilities, then our selves with their demands and denials emerge again in full regalia. It is easy to find peace in an artificially created silence within the mind, but to carry that peace into the world requires self-knowledge, which is something that cannot be discovered in the silence of isolation. The self can only be seen

through action, as it compares, judges, and projects itself—as it is hurt or flattered. We can only see the reality of anger or hatred, fear or deception, in the present moment, as they are happening. Any other inquiry into the self or its nature is not observation, but is rather an analysis of the past, of actions committed to memory, and we cannot come to reality through memory. The present moment is the only reality, and observation in the present moment is the only action that can show us the truth of ourselves.

Thus we must somehow bring the silence of meditation into the world of action, into the world of relationship, so that we may see, with full clarity, the fundamental form and substance of our selves in action.

Active meditation techniques do exist—techniques that we can perform in the midst of relationship, while participating in the world. Most of these are open-eye meditations, an important quality if we wish to function in the world of action through meditation. Ujjayi meditation is one such technique.

Chapter 19

Ujjayi Meditation

Jidhu Krishnamurti once said that true meditation is the opposite of concentration and mental discipline. He insisted, in fact, that no meditation exists other than the constant watchfulness of each moment as it occurs. He warned that the various techniques of mental control—the control of thought—carried the risk of narrowing the mind and providing fuel for the ego's false quest for spiritual growth. Many others have echoed his sentiments. It is easy to delude ourselves into believing, in those moments of artificial silence produced by suppressing thought to the point of nonexistence, that we have reached the ultimate reality—god, truth, or whatever. Indeed, such moments bring an experienced bliss. But this is not the bliss that flowers into the infinite unfolding of life—the bliss that occurs when the self knows itself for what it is.

If meditation is to be of any help, then it must do no more than clear obstacles from the path to truth. Reaching the truth is the real work. We must walk on the path once it is cleared. It is as though we have a window on reality, but it is fogged over, and through it we see only hazy images. If we clear the window with meditation, we must still look through it and make sense of what we see, or wiping the window served no purpose. Yet most of us, through meditation, clear the window and then turn our backs on the view that appears. We do this because the clear perception of our selves reveals profound ugliness and we immediately look away, or because we want to change what we see and thus begin again the unending and futile struggle with ourselves—that same struggle that originally created the ugliness. We deny ourselves, or we go to war with ourselves. Either way, it is the end of meditation and the fresh beginning of ignorance.

Thus we must be clear about the value of meditation, or else we will end up even deeper in our conflict and confusion.

Ujjayi meditation is done at all times with open eyes. To begin, sit quietly in a comfortable, upright, but relaxed position; if you are comfortable with padmasana (the lotus pose), that will work. Begin the basic Ujjayi breathing. After the breath evens out and settles down, begin to pay close attention to the outgoing breath. Watch its smooth, even character. Notice the slight friction of air in the back of the throat and the absence of friction in the nasal passages. Notice any characteristics that come to your attention during the exhalations. As you do this, you will find your mind wandering. At some point you will become aware that you are thinking instead of observing the breath. Gently, and without judgment of any kind, label the thought that came into your awareness; label it "thinking," and then return your awareness to the outgoing breath.

This cycle may happen a dozen times a minute; it doesn't matter. We are not trying to suppress thoughts; we simply want to be aware of them as they occur. The labeling process helps condition the mind to look for thoughts.

It may happen that you become lost in thought for a long period of time. You may suddenly become aware that you are thinking and notice that you have not watched the breath for many minutes. Again, it doesn't matter. What matters is that you are aware that you haven't been aware. Again, label the time lost in thought as "thinking," and gently return the awareness to the outgoing breath.

So far I haven't mentioned the incoming breath. During the in-breath we are simply waiting, nothing more. It's as though we just dialed a phone number and are waiting for the person to answer. This lack of instruction is purposeful; during the in-breath we have no task. We have nothing to watch, nothing to control, nothing to discipline. We are left to our own devices; we are left to ourselves.

Throughout the meditation stay with the basic Ujjayi breath. Don't attempt to do the full Ujjayi breathing. It is too much, at least at the beginning, to add the seesaw technique to your already overburdened thoughts.

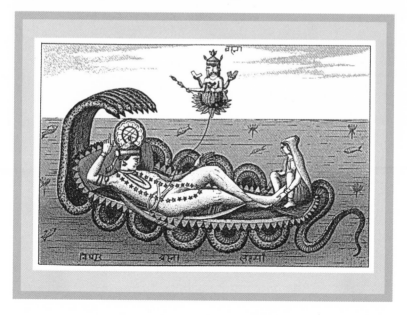

It is important that the labeling process continue. Each and every time you become aware that you are having thoughts, gently label them "thinking" and return to the outgoing breath. If you find yourself becoming frustrated or impatient with the persistence of your thoughts, then simply step back with the awareness and notice that the frustration or impatience is, in fact, also a thought. Label it and gently return to the breath. Through this process you will discover that all feelings occur hand in hand with thought. It is a powerful discovery.

The eyes stay open during the entire meditation. Simply look in the direction that you're facing and allow the eyes to fix comfortably on any object within your vision. Don't mentally investigate whatever you focus on; simply allow the eyes to rest wherever they will.

When you feel comfortable with the mechanics of Ujjayi meditation, sit quietly and meditate for at least 20 minutes. Eventually we will do Ujjayi meditation in the midst of activities, but to start, sit alone in a quiet space.

For the first few weeks of practice, remain sitting alone while you meditate. After it has become second nature, you can begin to bring the meditation into activity.

Your first experiments with Ujjayi meditation in activity should be in situations that are non-threatening and don't cause great emotional strife. A walk in the woods is a good first activity. Simply breathe, notice the out-breath, and label thoughts as they occur. You will find that rather than hinder your activities, the meditation will give you greater power to focus as your daydreams and other distracting thoughts gradually diminish on their own. Try to do the meditation twenty to thirty minutes each day.

You can progress from walking in the woods to walking downtown. From there you can graduate to doing your hobbies, working on the car, or any other solitary activity. You will find that you can meditate quite easily while performing complex activities with no degradation in efficiency or safety. When you are comfortable with meditation in solitary activities, it is time for the true test—meditating while interacting with others. This step is a bit tricky because, obviously, you cannot maintain the Ujjayi breathing while you talk. It's best to begin interacting with others in situations that don't require talking—watching a movie with a friend, listening to a lecture, attending a sporting event, sitting next to a stranger on a bus or plane. You will find that much of your self will surface even in these subtle interactions while you are silent.

Try to spend at least twenty minutes a day in such meditations.

Finally, you are ready to handle situations where you are interacting and talking.

By now you should be so comfortable with the Ujjayi meditation that you can begin and end it at will, effortlessly. The subtlest effort of will, almost imperceptible, is all that should be needed—similar to the effort of will needed to scratch your nose when it itches. When you are at this point, strike up an innocuous conversation with someone. It doesn't matter with whom, as long as the conversation doesn't lead to a hostile or fearful conclusion. While the other person is speaking, do your meditation. Keep your Ujjayi subtle and smooth so that the other person doesn't think you have a breathing disorder. When it is your turn to speak, stop the meditation. Continue this cycle for a few minutes. The alternating rhythm of meditation and talking should seem quite natural. In fact, you will notice that the rhythm of meditating and not meditating is identical to the rhythm of paying attention to the outgoing breath and waiting during the incoming breath. Again, spend at least twenty minutes a day meditating in this way, but don't get carried away. Limit it to no more than thirty minutes a day.

You might ask at this point, "Why would I want to do all of this?" The answer is in the doing. As you bring the Ujjayi meditation into your activities, a subtle but profound change takes place in the clarity of your perceptions, and the substance of the meditation itself begins to change. At some point the "watching" and the "waiting" rhythms of the meditation merge into a single experience. Further, the Ujjayi breathing becomes more and more difficult to distinguish from normal breathing. Eventually the meditation as a separate activity simply fades away, and you are left with only the "watching." At this point, meditation has become your way of life. *This* is the purpose and the value of the process.

Chapter 20

Breath and Relationship

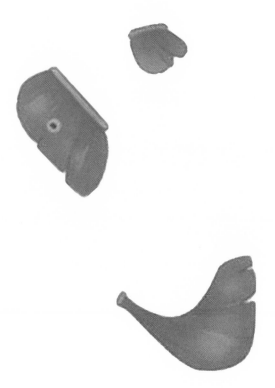

If we lived in complete isolation, in a cave perhaps, we would find little cause for anger and jealousy. Our greed would be limited to our immediate needs. Our lust would have no object and would soon wither. We would have no one else with whom we could compare ourselves, so ambition and envy would have no fuel. In short, we would be living in a state of minimal conflict. But isolation is not the path to truth. Isolation provides no stimulus for self-knowledge. On the contrary, it provides very little stimulus at all, and thus causes a gradual drift into a state of nonliving. Those who live in isolation may eventually report a sense of bliss, but by isolating themselves they cannot truly know the infinite depth and beauty of the world. Isolation is not the answer.

For those of us who do not live in caves, we daily face the unending conflicts of humanity. In any given day we feel, to some degree, every known emotion. Our anger is aroused by things that do not even directly touch us—news of national politics, injustice in some part of the world, an Oscar for a movie we despised. Fear is our constant companion. It rises at every corner with questions and suspicions: fear of being found out for something we have hidden, fear of losing our jobs or our families or our wealth, fear of death or injury. And

then there is the unending stream of petty jealousies, hurts to our pride, and missed pleasures.

What happens to us during any of these emotional upheavals? The power of the emotion takes control and we act without awareness, without thought. The more powerful the emotion, the less aware we become, and the more thoughtlessly we act. We become lost. These are the times when we can experiment with our newfound mastery of Ujjayi meditation.

Try the following: At the next opportunity to observe within yourself an emotional upheaval, such as anger or fear, no matter how large or small, watch what happens to your breathing. This should be quite easy, as you have spent weeks observing your breath during yoga practice and bringing it back to Ujjayi. The reflex to observe the breath should be strongly conditioned. If you have diligently practiced your breathing during your yoga sessions, you will instantly notice the irregularity and unnatural quality of the breath caused by the emotional upheaval you are experiencing. Immediately begin the Ujjayi meditation and notice what happens. The internal chaos quickly evaporates. As the emotion disappears, stop the Ujjayi meditation and simply observe. If the emotion and irregular breathing return, then return to the meditation. You can experiment with this at any time and with any upheaval in your daily relationships. You will soon find yourself taking a natural interest in the experimentation, and it will begin to take on a life of its own.

While experimenting with the breath, it is important that you become fully aware of the state of your irregular breath before beginning your Ujjayi. If you overlook this step, you will not perceive the process with full clarity.

If this process were nothing more than entertainment, it would have little value. But you will discover a growing awareness of yourself as you continue to experiment. As fear, jealousy, and anger evaporate, you are left with the simple facts that caused the emotion. We normally don't see them clearly because the overwhelming power of the emotion veils the reality behind it. But as the emotion dissipates more quickly, the residual reality comes into sharper focus. And, as a pleasant side effect, we become calmer and less likely to act out unpleasant feelings, so our friends, families, and even strangers are nicer to us.

However, remember to guard against the comfortable feeling that the meditation does anything whatsoever to bring you to a state of self-understanding. This slip is a great danger. The meditation is a powerful tool, and the self always prefers to expand itself rather than to look at itself. The self would be more than happy to use this tool to expand its own self-importance. Meditation merely clarifies the instruments of perception. You must still have the courage to look. The true work is in the observation of the self.

Chapter 21

The Understanding

Relational Yoga is a simple process, but each step in the process is important. A mastery of Ujjayi breathing is fundamental. Next, implementing Ujjayi in your yoga practice is absolutely necessary in order for you to integrate the breath with the natural movement of the body and to disconnect it from your emotional state. Then the basic Ujjayi technique must be mastered before you can bring the meditation into your activities. And finally, after you become proficient with meditation in action, you must learn to observe.

Self-observation is one of the most difficult things to master. As perception becomes clearer through improved harmony within the body, we begin to see ourselves more clearly in our relationships to life. We see the pettiness of our anger, the absurdity of our envies, and the emptiness behind our ambition. And then, what generally happens? Our basic instinct is to change it. We want to fix ourselves, improve ourselves, rid ourselves of our unwanted or embarrassing aspects. But when that happens, we simply move back into the world of the tiny self that perpetually seeks enlargement. Once we move from observation to a desire to change what we observe, the observation ceases. We are no longer observing: we are planning, choosing, working yet again to become something else, something greater and more perfect. This is

again the realm of that pitiful self we seek to understand. Instead of understanding, we thrust ourselves back into the world of constantly becoming, into the time-bound world of the self, into the world of craving for the future.

The purpose of observation is understanding. We are not observing ourselves so that we can change into something else. We are observing so that we can see the truth of our selves, in the moment, in the now. That understanding is itself the change. All other change is merely deception of the self—a return to a world of past and future where the empty, bankrupt self believes it can become something more than it is. Thus the challenge in observation is to observe without the desire to change what you observe, to become aware without judging.

Such discipline is not simple, obviously, but it is possible. It requires a constant alertness, without any semblance of control. The alertness itself is the key. For example, assume we are angry and, through our meditations, we see the pettiness of the anger. We then instantly judge the anger—that it is bad—and immediately initiate plans to eradicate such pettiness permanently from our lives. At this point, rather than chide ourselves for moving away from the simple task of observing, we can simply observe our wish to chide ourselves. We can observe our sense of defeat and frustration at not being able to maintain discipline. We simply step back and continue observing. All that has changed is the object of our observations. It was initially our anger; now it is our frustration. We only have to stay alert. No controlling or dis-ciplining of the result of our observations is necessary.

Alertness is what we cultivate through our meditations. It is the most subtle and yet the most powerful tool that we pos-sess. Through this alertness we have the power to observe. Through observation we reach understanding. And through understanding, real and profound change occurs.

Chapter 22

The Practice of Relational Yoga

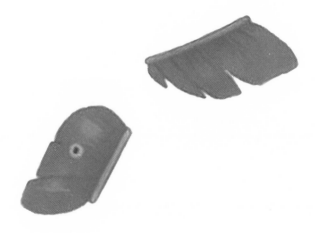

Relational Yoga is a system of practices that brings the stillness of yoga into the movement and conflicts of our daily life. It focuses on relationship as a mechanism of profound change—not just relationships to our loved ones, but our relationship to all of life.

Relational yoga is independent of the type of asanas you do, or specific school of yoga that you follow. The flexibility, strength, improved health, and bodily awareness afforded through any of the existing yoga schools is more or less the same. Relational Yoga provides:

- The harmonious connection of the breath to the movement of the body
- The disconnection of the breath from our emotional state
- The ability to experience active meditation
- The ability to bring the silence of meditative awareness into relational activities—into the world of action.

Relational Yoga is composed of five practices:

1. Basic yoga asanas
2. The Ujjayi breathing technique
3. Basic Ujjayi Meditation
4. Relational Ujjayi Meditation

5. Choiceless, nonjudgmental self-observation.

Each of these has been explained, to some extent, in the previous chapters.

Anyone can practice Relational Yoga. If you are currently not practicing any type of yoga, then you can buy a book, a videotape, or enroll yourself into a local yoga school to learn the basic postures. Once you are practicing yoga postures of any kind, no matter how basic, you can begin to apply the practice of Relational Yoga.

Yoga teachers who may be interested in Relational Yoga training courses for themselves can contact:

The Relational Yoga Mandiram
2000 Arapaho Street
Woodland Park, Colorado 80863

Phone: 719 687 8642
Email: support@woodlandpublications.com

Chapter 23

Further Inquiry

For many, the brief foundations described here will only whet the appetite and raise additional questions. Once you have begun the process of self-discovery in earnest, however, you will find that no help can be forthcoming from outside yourself. All questions originate within you, and only your self can provide the answers. No one else can lead you to your self. No one can show you your inner structures, your web of fear and desire. No one can impart wisdom or give you some mystical revelation.

It is important that you accept no authority on your journey of self-discovery. We should each treat "helpful" hints, including everything we have read in this book and every other book, with an attitude of skepticism. If something is true, then it is in yourself—you can validate it for yourself. No guru or spiritual master is necessary to show you what is true. The reality of ourselves can only be seen in relationship to the present moment, and that relationship is itself the guru. Through that relationship the true or the false in any experience, statement, or concept can be seen. It requires only simple, nonjudgmental self-observation. If someone tells you or implies: "I *know*, and you do not," then that person is living in a divided world—a world of duality—and you could invite that person to join you on your journey.

But the most dangerous authority to avoid is our own. We are each filled with a complex web of dead experiences that gives us the formulas by which we judge and act. These formulas make up our inner authority. It is these formulas—past knowledge, memories, fear responses, hardened judgments—that have created our conflicts and present confusion. Authority is the past. Our inner authority is no more a guidepost than someone else's authority. The truth of ourselves is there to be seen in the moment. It is in front of us. No authority is necessary for us to be able to glimpse and understand it.

And, lastly, beware of words, for they can become a danger. We live behind the line that separates the "I" from the world—the line that we have created. It is a narrow space, bounded and contained by restrictive borders. It is a finite space, and words—which have a finite meaning in the tiny realm of our memories and mental images—are themselves finite. Yet we are observing and attempting to understand something that goes far beyond the narrow boundaries that we have artificially established. It is an unbounded reality— infinite and timeless; but, since words and concepts are finite and bounded, any *description* of this must be a vague approximation and will be certain to contain contradictions. Words like "journey," "seeker," "path," and so forth can become traps. If we are on a *journey* of self-discovery, then the true journey *is* the destination. The first step of the journey is the last step; the beginning is the end. If we are *seekers,* then the true seeking must have no object, no *result.* If we begin to seek a result, an end, then we are no longer observing—we have stopped self-observation and have begun searching for something in the future. If we are seeking *something,* no matter what that object may be, then we are denying the reality that is in front of us—clear, in the present moment, for how can you search for what is in front of you? The fact that you are searching implies that the object is elsewhere. When we seek to discover our selves, we must attempt to perceive the reality *behind* the words that we use. A word is a symbol—it is not the thing.

You have embarked on the loneliest of journeys. It is not a journey of isolation or separation, for you are moving for the first time outside of your self-imposed isolation and separation. But it is nevertheless a journey in which you are entirely alone.

You have with you only the tools of which you have some mastery and which you choose to apply to the work. And you have your self. There are obviously additional tools. One such tool may or may not prove fruitful and be in harmony with your individuality. It is a "quick cleanse" for the windows of perception. It is not for everyone, however, and it does create a considerable shock to the system. It first surfaced in a twelfth century A.D. yoga text called the *Goraksha-Samhita*. This text describes in detail a technique, based on the respiratory cycle, called the gayatri so-ham. It has been refined through the passage of time by the Kriya school of yoga and is now called kriya kundalini pranayama. Other common names are hamsa kriya, so-ham kriya, and nagaraj pranayama. A group not affiliated with the Kriya tradition, called the Art of Living Foundation, also teaches the technique under the name of sudarshan kriya. It is an extraordinarily powerful breathing technique that uses alternating breath rhythms as its base. The practice, in a matter of hours, brings you to a state of complete internal stillness, which lasts for a considerable period. It is difficult to find a knowledgeable teacher, however, as the technique is seldom used today outside of a few small schools. But you can contact an Art of Living center in your area, or almost any Kriya yoga organization, if you wish to pursue it.

Beyond this prospect, you are on your own, literally and in the deepest sense.

*Y*e shall know the truth, and the truth shall make you free.

John 8:32

Appendix A

Ujjayi Breathing

Ujjayi breathing is the foundation of most yogic breathing techniques, or pranayamas. Ujjayi means "uprising," which refers to the upward movement of the breath energy when done properly.

Ujjayi breathing has three characteristics:

1. A distinctive Ujjayi sound
2. An even flow of the breath
3. A distinctive "wave" motion of the diaphragm.

Of these three, the Ujjayi sound is the most important for proper technique. If we believe we are breathing in Ujjayi fashion but do not hear the distinctive sound, then we are probably not doing it correctly.

To begin breathing using the Ujjayi breath, first sit comfortably in a quiet location so that you are able to hear the sound of your breathing. Then draw in the air through both nostrils while holding the glottis—the vocal diaphragm in the back of the throat—partially closed. This partial closure produces a sound similar to quiet snoring, or ocean waves heard from a distance. Some people describe the sound as an "ahhh," or a quiet sobbing sound, or a deep hissing. The sound should be smooth, continuous, and unbroken during the entire inhale. It's as if you are whispering the sound "haaaa" in the back of the throat. The breath is done through both nostrils on both inhale and exhale, with the mouth closed. Keep the glottis partially closed at all times during the breathing, so that the sound is heard on both inhalation and exhalation.

When you first begin, it is helpful to pretend that you are fogging a mirror. Hold the palm of your hand in front of your mouth and imagine that it is a mirror. Exhale gently through the open mouth onto the palm of your hand as though trying to fog the mirror. Pay attention to the whispering sound that your breath makes. It is a hissing, "haaaa" sound. Do this a number of times and focus on the sound of your breath as you continue to fog the mirror. Then close your mouth and try to fog the mirror with the breath from your nostrils, continuing to make the soft whispering hiss. Pay attention to the tightening of the glottis in the back of your throat. When you are comfortable with the exhalation through the nostrils, try to make the same sound on inhalation, continuing to constrict the glottis. The sound should be low and uniform throughout the breathing. It is actually a pleasant sound when done properly. This is the basic Ujjayi breath.

In Ujjayi, the sensation of breathing—the friction of air—should be entirely in the back of the throat. You should feel no air friction within the nostrils, and no nasal sounds should be heard. It's as if you are breathing through your throat instead of through your nostrils. Some people even describe the sensation as breathing through the ears—but not everyone, so don't panic if you don't feel this.

When you feel you understand the process, breathe gently with the basic Ujjayi breath for five or ten minutes at a time to begin conditioning yourself to the breath. After some practice sessions, you should be able to return to the basic breath any time that you choose. It is like riding a bicycle—once you can do it, you never forget it.

We can now move to the second part of Ujjayi breathing: the even flow of the breath.

If you observe your normal breath you will see that for both inhalation and exhalation, the breath begins fast and then slows and tapers off toward the end of the breath. As we become excited or agitated, this variance between the beginning and ending of the breath becomes more pronounced. With Ujjayi, we keep the breath continuous, uniform and smooth throughout the entire process. The yogic traditions describe the Ujjayi as an unbroken flow of light clear oil, so steady that even in motion it appears motionless. It should be clear, smooth and almost silky in its quality.

With each inhalation and exhalation, the volume of air should remain the same per period of time. Regulating this pace of the breath will be slightly difficult at first, but with time it becomes second nature. It is helpful to listen to the sound of the Ujjayi. As the pace speeds up or slows down, the sound will vary accordingly, so by listening to the variance you can learn to bring the breath back into a constant flow.

It is important that we don't constrict the glottis to the point that it causes tension in the throat or anywhere in the head. The breathing should be easy and fluid.

When the flow of breath becomes smooth and even, we can move to the third part of Ujjayi breathing: the wave motion of the diaphragm.

This part of the Ujjayi is frequently called the "seesaw" breath, because it resembles the motion of a seesaw. Begin by pulling the navel in and filling the very top of the chest at the beginning of the inhalation, then slowly move the inhalation down until the lower belly is the last part to expand. On exhalation, compress the lower belly first by pulling the navel up and back toward the spine, then slowly move the exhalation up until the upper chest is the last to exhale.

These three characteristics comprise the full Ujjayi breath. If you have difficulty coordinating these aspects, or if you are in a period of low energy or poor health, simply return to the basic Ujjayi breath until you feel more comfortable using the full Ujjayi.

List of Illustrations

Page   **Illustration**

xii . . . . . Heironmous Bosch
14 . . . . . The nymphs of the Milk Sea
16 . . . . . Mythic camel
22 . . . . . The Hindoo symbol of creation
29 . . . . . Brahma the creative power
32 . . . . . Buddha-Surya
38 . . . . . Brahm, wrapped in the Maya
40 . . . . . Martin Shongauer
42 . . . . . Vishnu as man-lion
44 . . . . . Temple of Miroc in Japan
50 . . . . . Buddha
56 . . . . . Indian idol of Astrachan
59 . . . . . Idol of Lamaism
68 . . . . . The Lingam
69 . . . . . Japanese idol
75 . . . . . Buddha
76 . . . . . The Dreams
82 . . . . . Svantevit
84 . . . . . The tortoise supporting the world
88 . . . . . Idol of Lamaism
90 . . . . . Statue of Osiris
94 . . . . . Vishnu as Kaninki or Katki
96 . . . . . The giant Garuda
101 . . . . . Hindoo idol
103 . . . . . Javanese idol

Page   **Illustration**

114 . . . . . The Maya as Bhavani
116 . . . . . Pracriti
128 . . . . . Siva as Rudra
130 . . . . . Camadeva or Camos
139 . . . . . Vishnu
142 . . . . . Brahma and Saravadi
146 . . . . . Siva, the destroying power
153 . . . . . Birth of Brahma
155 . . . . . Vishnu as a tortoise
156 . . . . . The giant Ravana
162 . . . . . Javanese idol
163 . . . . . Siva on the giant Muyelagin
168 . . . . . The Trimurti
169 . . . . . Vishnu as a fish
174 . . . . . Javanese idol
178 . . . . . Javanese idol
181 . . . . . Albrecht Durer

Other Books by the Author

The Secret of the Yamas
A Spiritual Guide to Yoga

The Fabric of Self
The Spirit of Relational Yoga